PENGUIN BOOKS

HUNTER KILLER

Born in Glasgow, Harry McCallion joined the army after leaving school. In a varied and exciting military career he served with the Parachute Regiment, South Africa's elite Recce Commandos and 22 SAS. After leaving the army in 1985 he joined the RUC, but left in 1990 after a near-fatal car crash. Subsequent to this he studied law and was called to the Bar. Now a working barrister and writer he has recently received his Master's Degree in International Relations. His autobiography *Killing Zone* was an immediate bestseller.

Hunter Killer

HARRY McCALLION

PENGUIN BOOKS

PENGUIN BOOKS

Published by the Penguin Group
Penguin Books Ltd, 27 Wrights Lane, London w8 5tz, England
Penguin Books USA Inc., 375 Hudson Street, New York, New York 10014, USA
Penguin Books Australia Ltd, Ringwood, Victoria, Australia
Penguin Books Canada Ltd, 10 Alcorn Avenue, Toronto, Ontario, Canada m4v 3b2
Penguin Books (NZ) Ltd, 182–190 Wairau Road, Auckland 10, New Zealand

Penguin Books Ltd, Registered Offices: Harmondsworth, Middlesex, England

First published 1998
1 3 5 7 9 10 8 6 4 2

Set in 10.5/12.5pt Monotype Fournier
Typeset by Intype London Ltd
Printed in England by Clays Ltd, St Ives plc

I

The pale sun hid behind a low bank of greyish clouds, as if unsure whether to rise. Even the thin drizzle was half-hearted, hardly penetrating the foliage of the tall forest. Only the river showed urgency. It cut between the pines to cascade over a rocky ledge and plunge forty feet to the valley below. Overnight there had been a violent storm in the hills, fuelling the torrent. A red deer paused to drink from the clear water. Abruptly the doe's head came up and she disappeared with speed into the trees.

Seconds later a man appeared. He came over the ridge low and fast, moving swiftly towards the river's edge. Dropping flat, he took quick gulps of water and then looked back in the direction from which he'd come. He turned next to the river. It was too deep to ford. A line of flat stones near the edge offered a possible crossing point, though it would briefly expose him to the valley.

He was just over halfway across when a sharp crack broke the silence. Pain: searing, white-hot agony, then darkness, but still the pain burning in his head. He was falling through space, the air rushing past his tumbling body. Perhaps he would fall for ever. The water hit him with immense force, punching out what air remained in his lungs in a muffled scream. He was aware of his body sinking in the icy water.

His feet hit the bottom. His eyes were open now and above him he could dimly see daylight. With all his remaining strength he kicked out towards it. He moved as if in slow motion, his arms flailing like windmill sails.

His head broke the surface. He drew one long, shuddering breath into his screaming lungs, then his head was pulled back under. The thick parka he wore was dragging him down, but when he tussled with the zip it jammed. He wrenched his arms out of the sleeves, one at a time, then forced the waterlogged jacket over his head. He broke the surface again and this time stayed afloat, gasping.

As his senses returned, he saw the bank a bare ten feet away and struggled towards it with a laboured breast-stroke. There he clung on to the grasses that sprouted from the earth above his head. Slowly his breathing returned to normal as he listened to the low thundering of the waterfall. Even in his exhausted state it didn't take long to realize how lucky he'd been to miss the jagged rocks at its base. He felt the pain in his head again and ran his hand across it. There was a deep wound along his right temple.

Then he heard voices. He hugged the bank and slipped deeper into the water.

'You sure you got him?' The voice, unmistakably American, was deep and rasping with irritation.

'Well sure, Frank. I haven't missed a target at less than a hundred yards in my life. I hit him all right.'

The second speaker had a lazy southern US drawl.

'Where's the goddamn body then, Ray?'

They were standing directly above him, hidden from view by the slight overhang.

'Who gives a shit? He's dog meat, for sure. You saw him fall, same as me. If my bullet didn't kill him the fall woulda.'

2

There was less conviction in the other man's voice as he said, 'Braxton wants this fella's head.'

'I know, I know. The water's pretty fast-flowing, probably carried the body downstream a way. We'll find it wedged against one of the banks where it narrows . . .'

He waited for their footsteps to fade before raising his head carefully above the bank. A well-trodden path wound along the margin of the river and into the forest. He strained his eyes and ears, finally satisfying himself he was alone before trying to drag himself across the overhang. It was harder than he thought it would be: his legs were numb and his body sapped of strength by the fall and the chill of the water. On the third attempt he managed it. He hoped the Americans were a good distance away. The cold was starting to become a more dangerous enemy. He rubbed his arms and legs vigorously.

Gingerly, he touched his scalp. It was a close call: another inch to the left and it would have been goodnight Irene. He stopped rubbing as it struck him quite suddenly that that was all he could remember: pain, a fall, the water, a snatch of conversation. But before that, nothing. It was like peering into a dark night in which vague shadows shifted and moved. Questions cluttered his mind. Where was he? Why were they trying to kill him? He touched his scalp again, realizing that the bullet that had so nearly ended his life had robbed him of his memory.

He searched his pockets for identification, but found nothing. His wallet must have been in the parka he'd discarded. Around his waist was a thick belt holding two pouches, a water bottle and a knife. He pulled out the knife; it was a bone-handled Bowie, the blade a full eight inches long. He tested the edge – razor-sharp. He checked the pouches. They contained a survival kit: snares, matches in waterproof bags, scalpels, a mirror, a pencil torch, aspirin, codeine, antiseptic powder and two bottles of coloured tablets marked 'anti-fever' and 'anti-diarrhoea'; but no food, unfortunately. Whoever I am, he thought, I'm no idiot.

He strapped the belt back around his waist and stood to look around. The trees still had all their leaves, although they were starting to turn brown. It was cold but not freezing. Probably early autumn. He shook his head. He had to get away from here before the two men returned.

But which way to go? He looked up at the top of the waterfall. In other circumstances he'd have been awed by its beauty. He shrugged and headed back uphill. In the distance, he could see the beginnings of a range of mountains. 'Always take the high ground,' a voice he didn't recognize whispered in his mind.

Forty minutes later he was back at the top of the fall. The climb had been steep but he felt exhilarated. It was good to be alive. He glanced back and then threw himself flat. The men were back, studying the bank where he'd clambered out. Seconds later they looked up towards his position. One unclipped a compact two-way radio from his belt.

'Manuel, this is Frank. Over.'

'Go ahead, Frank.'

The man's heart missed a beat, his stomach contracted; he could hear every word. Manuel was close, very close.

'Looks like our boy is still alive. His name's Fraser – we found some ID in his coat. Ray must just have winged him. We've found where he left the river and it looks like he's heading back up toward you. You got that?'

'*Sí, amigo*. I heard something a few minutes back. I thought it was you. I'll take a closer look now.'

The man lay where he had dropped, hardly daring to breathe. Fraser, Fraser: the name echoed in his mind, meaning little. He heard the sound of Manuel putting his radio away. He was about to start inching his way back down the slope when the man stepped into view. He carried a Kalashnikov AK47 assault rifle parallel with his body, the butt inches from his shoulder. From this 'high port' position a trained man could fire a shot at a snap target in under a second. Manuel looked like a trained man.

They saw each other at the same instant. As Manuel brought the weapon to bear, Fraser launched his body forward like a steel spring. He hit Manuel with every ounce of his twelve-stone frame, knocking him backwards. He drove his shoulder into the gunman's solar plexus, driving the breath from his lungs. The rifle flew from Manuel's hands and landed a yard away. Fraser drew himself up to deliver a finishing blow, only to feel the man's knee drive into his ribs. He let out a bellow of pain. His blow, intended for his opponent's throat, landed ineffectively on his chest. Manuel's body arched. He found himself sailing through the air, to land heavily on his back. He rolled quickly to get to his feet, and was able to see his enemy's face clearly for the first time. A low brow, slanting, coal-black eyes, a broad, flattened nose above a knife slash of a mouth. Mexican, with a dash of Indian blood. Manuel's eyes drifted to the left and Fraser followed his gaze. The AK47 was too far away for either to reach. Manuel's smile was more animal than human, revealing two rows of perfect white teeth. Then he bent swiftly and from the top of his boot snatched a twin-edged fighting knife.

Almost without thinking, Fraser unsheathed the Bowie at his waist. Manuel's eyes narrowed slightly as he began to edge slowly forward. Fraser crouched, holding his knife with the blade extended upwards from his right hand, his thumb behind the protective guard. He kept it rock still.

Manuel's knife arm moved constantly, weaving a deadly web as it criss-crossed before him. Fraser looked deep into the man's emotionless eyes. Manuel returned his stare with reptilian intensity. 'Don't look at his eyes, you idiot,' a voice shouted in his brain. 'Watch the knife. Nobody stabs you with their eyes.' The shock of the phantom command made him take a half-step backwards and he switched his gaze to his opponent's knife. Manuel interpreted the reaction as fear and began to advance.

'Watch the knife, block the first strike and look for an opening. Make your first strike decisive.'

Manuel continued to move forward, supremely confident now. He feigned a strike. Once, twice. Then, with frightening speed, he struck a sweeping slash towards his enemy's throat. Fraser blocked. The knives met in a jarring clash of tempered steel and sparks, sending shock waves up their knife arms. For a second both men froze, so close that they could smell each other's breath, then, in a movement so graceful it could have been choreographed, Fraser transferred his weight and ducked so that Manuel's knife passed over his head. Even as the Mexican tried to counter his strike, Fraser used the power of his thigh muscles to drive his own body upright again and the Bowie to the hilt in his adversary's stomach. He felt the hot gush of gastric gases pass over his hand. Manuel let out a single grunt of pain, then slid towards the ground, all but dragging Fraser's knife from his hand.

There was surprisingly little blood. Moving quickly, Fraser unzipped the Mexican's heavy jacket and stripped off the shoulder holster and Browning 9mm automatic pistol. The jacket fitted well. In its left hip pocket was a spare magazine for the AK47; the right held a compact two-way radio. The dead man had a sweet tooth. There were two chocolate bars in one of the top pockets. Fraser picked up the rifle and moved off.

Twenty minutes later he paused to eat one of the bars and take a drink of water. Around him the dense forest was quiet. He pulled out and turned on the two-way radio.

'Manuel, this is Frank, over.'

Silence. His two friends from the river hadn't found the dead Mexican yet.

'Frank, this is Tony. We're moving in from the north, so watch out for us. Over.'

Then a new voice said, 'Roger that, Tony. We've lost contact with Manuel, can't think . . . Jesus H Christ . . .'

'What's wrong, Frank? Over.'

'He's dead – knifed. His guns are gone, and his jacket.'

The radio net disintegrated into a confused babble. Fraser judged that there were probably five small groups searching for him, each demanding information.

'Everybody, calm down and get off the air.' This was a voice of authority, a voice that radiated confidence and reassurance.

'Frank, this is Matt. Stay calm. Send me a grid ref of your present location. Over.'

He heard Frank give the six-figure map reference.

'Roger that, Frank. Now, listen in, all stations. I want radio silence until further notice. Out.'

Five groups acknowledged briefly. Then nothing.

A lot of men were trying to kill him. Somehow Fraser knew that this wasn't the first time. He looked at the greying sky, and calculated there was about an hour and a half of daylight left. He wanted some distance between himself and the owner of that voice.

*

Twenty minutes later three men topped the rise above the waterfall. Two were well above average height. A shaven-headed black with the physique of a wrestler led the way. Framed by a mane of jet-black hair held back by a band of green cloth, the features of the second man were those of a pure North American Indian.

As they drew level with the body, the third man said, 'OK, Billy. Have a look around.'

The Apache moved forward, studying the ground with the intensity of a scholar reading a book. He made a slow circle of the clearing, dropping occasionally to study the ground more closely. Finally, he ripped open the Mexican's shirt to observe the knife wound that had finished him.

'Manuel came from over there,' he said, pointing to the west. 'Our friend was lying here.' He pointed again. 'He charged Manuel and forced the rifle out of his hands. They had a knife fight. Manuel lost.'

'Hell, Billy,' Frank broke in, 'that don't seem likely. I mean, the greaser . . .' Frank broke off at the savage look from Billy. 'I mean, Manuel was pure poison with a knife. Only you were better.'

Billy shrugged, gesturing towards the corpse.

'Any chance he killed Manuel with his own knife?'

Billy shook his head. 'No, Mr Kirby. Manuel was killed with a Bowie knife. See?' He pointed to the wound in the Mexican's side. 'Jagged edges. Only one knife makes those wounds. Manuel carried a fighting knife . . . spear-point. It's still here and there's no blood on it.'

Kirby nodded. 'Whoever this guy Fraser is, he's no pilgrim, that's for sure. Can you track him?'

Billy glanced at the forest floor. 'Easy. He's making no effort to hide his tracks. He has nearly an hour's start on me.'

His eyes narrowed. 'That means he's about three miles in front.' He glanced towards the setting sun. 'Less than an hour of daylight left, so I won't catch up to him tonight. Be about midday tomorrow before I find him.' There was no bravado in the Indian's voice. It was a simple statement of fact.

'OK, Billy, head after him. I'll throw the rest of the boys out in a cordon along the unfenced corner of the estate. Take a radio. I'll have new ones issued so our friend can't listen in, but keep one set open on your call-sign. When you find him call me.'

The Apache shouldered his rifle, a new German Heckler & Koch G3, and turned to leave.

'Just a minute, Billy.' The tracker squatted on his heels as Kirby spoke into the radio. 'Hello, Mr Fraser, do you want to talk?' He paused. 'If you were smart enough to take Manuel's radio, you're smart enough to keep a listening watch on it. Why don't you just talk to us? Listen, buddy,' Kirby said, staring into the distant woods as he talked, 'none of this is my doing. I know you feel a sense of . . .' His voice trailed off as he searched for, then added, the right word: 'grievance'. Kirby glanced at the ring of faces before continuing. 'Getting yourself killed won't help anybody. You were lucky today, but we won't underestimate you again. Why don't you give me a call and we can work something out?'

All five men in the clearing stared at the radio for several seconds. It remained silent.

Kirby shook his head in exasperation. 'OK, buddy, if that's the way you want it. But I'll keep a listening watch if you want to come in.' He threw the radio to the black man, then looked at the Apache and drew his right thumb across his own throat.

Billy rose silently from his squatting position and faded into the woods like a wraith.

Fraser had listened, puzzled, to the soft voice. What was his sense of grievance? Through the mists of his memory something stirred, something important. But then it was gone.

After stashing the radio in Manuel's jacket, he set off. He had to keep moving – not just to evade capture but to generate body heat and dry his clothes out. The forest gave him excellent cover, but once darkness fell his passage through the dense undergrowth would be noisy. He knew from the moss on the tree trunks that he was heading in a northerly direction. It was richer and more abundant towards the side facing the sun, the south. Occasionally he crossed a track. He took special care here, stopping to listen for some thirty seconds before venturing across. No signs of life disturbed his progress.

It was dusk when Fraser reached the fence, which was double, twelve feet high, of chain-link construction and topped with three coils of razor wire. There was a run of about eight feet between the twin layers of fence, and thin metal wires ran through the entire length of both, to link up with junction boxes fixed to the support struts. Vibration detectors, no doubt linked to a central alarm system. A soft, whirring sound caused him to glance upwards. On top of the nearest support strut a closed-circuit video camera panned round in a tight arc. He swore under his breath and slipped back into the forest. The fence was probably patrolled, he decided, and there was little chance of scaling both layers before a reaction team arrived.

The shadows lengthened and a wave of tiredness swept over him. His feet ached. He unlaced his leather boots, stripped off his wet socks, wrung them out as dry as he could and then turned them inside out. From his medical kit he found antiseptic powder and sprinkled it liberally over the chafed areas on his feet. He replaced his socks and boots and instantly felt better. 'Always look after your feet,' his inner voice told him. 'They're the most important part of your body.'

He pulled the water bottle from his waist and drank again. His empty stomach gurgled. Fumbling in his top pocket, he found the other chocolate bar and ate it slowly. He knew it would be better to save it for later; but God, he was hungry, and afterwards his stomach still growled. His eyes were drawn to an outgrowth at about head height on the tree opposite. He walked over to inspect it.

It was a growth of fungus, with a deep blue-grey, shell-shaped cap nearly five inches in diameter. There was an abundance of others sprouting from nearby trees. He touched the nearest; its flesh was rubbery. He wondered if it was edible. Yes, something told him. As he plucked the fungus ideas tumbled through his mind. Nutritionally, fungi come between vegetables and meat in the food table. They contain more protein than vegetables, and fat. Many fungi have the same amount of calories as vegetables. Tree fungi are large and leathery and not harmful to humans. He turned the fungi around to study it; underneath it had white gills. Oyster fungus, *Pleurotus ostreatus*, he decided.

Without hesitation he picked an armful and retreated back to his tree. After discarding three that were discoloured, he skinned and sliced the fungi with the Bowie, then began to eat. Although tasty, they were rather tough and would have been better stewed, but he couldn't risk a fire so close to nightfall. As he ate he considered the conundrum that faced him.

It was clear that he could take care of himself. When he faced immediate danger or the need to survive, skills that were somehow ingrained in him were instantly activated. Yet he couldn't remember how he'd come to this place. Even his own name, Fraser, was unfamiliar to him. How could that be? He ran his fingers gently along the bullet crease in his temple. The hair above the wound was thick with congealed blood. Somehow his injury had robbed him of those memories that were part of his identity.

His skull was throbbing with pain. He needed to rest. Finishing the last of the fungi, he took another swig of water; at least his stomach felt full. He would sleep easier now, and crawled into a deep thicket to do so. Wrapping himself in the dead Mexican's jacket, he closed his eyes, forcing away the questions that gnawed at his mind. Right now he needed sleep more than answers.

It came quickly, releasing him from pain and fear. But with it came a kaleidoscope of dimly remembered faces and a cacophony of voices that called to him through a jumble of images. He slept fitfully, murmuring incomplete answers to the phantoms' half-formed questions. A woman's voice pierced the bedlam.

'Help me, help me.'

He ran towards the sound. Clawing hands ripped at him, preventing him from reaching her.

'I need you. Where are you? Please, please, I need you.'

He struggled frantically against the claws that held him. He screamed noiselessly at giant forms that kept him from her.

'You promised. You promised we'd always be together.'

In the distance he saw her indistinct white figure running to him, arms outstretched. Then the forms that held him closed in around her too, and she was gone. He faintly heard her voice one last time.

'*Help me.*'

Barely suppressing a scream, Fraser jerked upright, drawing the Browning without conscious thought. He glared about him in the darkness, swinging the pistol left and right, searching for a target, his thumb on the safety-catch, finger alongside the trigger guard.

Cold sweat poured down his face. He drew in deep, sharp gulps of air. His head swivelled swiftly from side to side as he searched for the woman who had so desperately called to him. He recoiled, seeing the giant hands from his nightmare closing in around him. Then he realized it was only the branches of the trees that surrounded him in the silent forest.

He rubbed a hand over his face. His mouth was dry, and a bitter taste cloyed at the back of his throat, forcing him to spit. Slowly his breathing returned to normal. Looking at his watch, he was surprised to find that he'd slept for barely twenty minutes. He pulled out his water bottle, rinsed his mouth and took a deep gulp of water, enjoying the coldness as it raced down his throat.

Shivering slightly, he lay back, his thoughts still dominated by the nightmare. He'd recognized the voice: it belonged to someone important to him, someone in trouble. He wished he could have seen the woman's face; perhaps he would have recognized her. Once again a wave of exhaustion swept over him and, as sleep threatened to engulf him once more, her plaintive voice drifted through his mind.

No wind stirred the trees around him. Gradually the haunting sound of his dream faded as the forest soothed him with its stillness. He gazed upwards through the branches into the crystal-clear night sky, which was lit by a bright three-quarter moon. He searched the constellations; Cassiopeia shaped like a giant 'W'. Orion, with its belt of three stars. Then he recognized the Plough, and swept along its familiar length to the two pointer stars, Dubhe and Merak. Measuring the distance between them and quadrupling it to find the Pole Star, he drew a mental line down from it to the ground. It confirmed that he'd been heading north all afternoon. It seemed as good a direction as any to follow in the morning.

Turning on to his side, he swiftly found sleep again.

2

Detective Chief Inspector Galbraith stepped out of the Highlands Police Land Rover and squinted at the dying sun as it
dipped below the tree line. He took a deep breath and burst
into a coughing fit, then fumbled in his pockets until he found
a packet of Capstan. As he shoved a cigarette in his mouth,
he threw a glance at the nervous young uniformed driver
who accompanied him.

Galbraith's face was creased with the sorrows its owner
had witnessed in his two decades of police service, making
him look much older than his forty-two years. Yet his soft
brown eyes still showed the humour that had always protected
him.

Looking up at the grey walls of the square, four-storey
mansion, he said, 'Looks more like a fortress, eh, Constable?'

McLeod House had been built with defence in mind. Its
builder, Red Hugh McLeod, had thrown his weight behind
George II during the ill-fated rebellion of the Young Pre-
tender, Bonnie Prince Charlie. His McLeods had worn the
hated red coat of the English army at Culloden and had
bayoneted the wounded Scots rebels to death after the battle.
His reward had been a great estate in the north-west highlands,
and the enduring hatred of his fellow-Scots.

Knowing his people, he had built his house of granite, with

walls four feet thick and a flat roof around which ran a chest-high buttress, giving excellent protection to a guard force. The entrance door, reached by two flights of steep stone steps, was of foot-thick oak, set in a deep recess with marksman's slots on either side. The surrounding forest had been cleared for two hundred yards in all directions. Red Hugh had built well, and his house had kept him safe.

The estate had passed from McLeod to McLeod until the beginning of the present century, when the last Lord, Angus McLeod, had been forced to sell it to fund his dissolute lifestyle. Thereafter, it had been the property of an Indian maharaja, an American film star and a louche English rock idol. Its present owner was Edward Braxton, an American entrepreneur and industrialist.

The original artisans could not have envisaged that the cleared ground would one day house a helicopter landing pad. Parked on this reinforced-concrete circle was a twelve-seater Sikorsky executive helicopter.

The short, stocky detective heard a whirring sound. Above the door a security camera was focusing on him. There were similar devices at the four corners of the building. He heard the sound of the great door being unlocked. As it opened, he didn't bother to conceal a look of distaste. Undeterred, Brian Hamilton advanced with a ready smile and an outstretched hand.

'Ian, this is a surprise. The guard rang to say you were on your way up to see us. What can I do for you?'

Galbraith ignored the outstretched hand. 'It's about the assault on the two Dunn boys and Andy Kerr. The Procurator-fiscal is dropping the charge against Manuel García.'

'That's good news. Manuel was very worried.'

'I'm sure he was. Stabbing a youngster and leaving him half dead was good for at least eight years.'

'That would have been a matter for the courts, of course.' Hamilton's voice remained congenial.

'It may not surprise you to hear that young Andy came in this morning and made a new statement. It was the Dunn boys who started the fight and he believes one of them stabbed him by mistake.'

Hamilton's smile broadened. 'Isn't that what I told you from the start?'

'A bunch of your highly trained thugs jump three eighteen-year-olds and put them in hospital. One has multiple stab wounds and a collapsed lung and now, two months later, another suddenly changes his story completely. I wonder why. Do you think the burden of telling a lie against the employees of the Laird of McLeod became too much to bear?'

Hamilton remained silent.

'I wasn't on duty this morning when Andy and his father Frank came in, so I went round this evening to see them, and guess what I found parked outside the house?'

Hamilton shrugged.

'A bloody Mercedes. It seems that Frank Kerr has gone into the taxi business. Now I wonder where a man like Kerr, who's never had two pennies to rub together, suddenly got the money to buy a £20,000 car?'

'Maybe he got a loan.' Hamilton's tone was less than convincing.

Galbraith took a final pull on his cigarette and observed Hamilton over its glowing tip. He exhaled the smoke through his nose and nodded slowly. 'Sure, and the cheque's in the post, there really is a Santa Claus and I won't come in your mouth.'

'I don't know what you're trying to suggest . . .'

'I'm not suggesting anything. Did you hear me suggest anything, Constable Lang?'

'No, sir,' Lang replied smartly.

'Constable Lang doesn't think I'm suggesting anything.'

There was silence between the two older men. Galbraith let it lie and enjoyed the discomfort on Hamilton's face. Finally he put a hand inside his tweed jacket and produced a manila envelope.

'Here's García's passport. The charges against your other two men still stand.' He moved closer to Hamilton. His voice was a whisper, inaudible to the watching constable. 'I don't like you, Hamilton. You were bent when you were on the job, you're bent now and one day I'm going to have your balls for breakfast.' He turned to leave.

Hamilton let him reach the door before he spoke. 'Anne sends her regards.'

Galbraith stopped in mid-stride, his body stiffening. The watching constable saw fury and anguish in his superior's face and for a second thought the detective would respond. Then he saw the mask drop back into place. Without a word or a backward glance Galbraith went down the steps and climbed into the police vehicle.

Hamilton watched as they disappeared along the forest track that led to the main gate three miles away. He tapped García's passport thoughtfully against his left hand. The exterior lights came on, jerking him into action. Just inside the door was a bank of CCTV monitors. Hamilton nodded to the man seated in front of them and got a curt acknowledgement.

He crossed the marble-floored hall to the newly installed

lift and pressed the button. The ground floor was the security section and also contained the kitchen, communal dining hall and gym. The first and second floors were the sleeping quarters for forty men. Braxton's offices, which had world-wide computer links to the divisions of Braxton Industries International, and the communications room, were on the third. The whole of the fourth floor was Braxton's private apartment.

The lift door slid back to reveal another security man, a carbon copy of the one below, standing to one side of heavy oak double doors. Without taking his eyes off Hamilton, he picked up a red phone and after a couple of seconds Hamilton heard a curt 'yes'.

'Mr Hamilton's here, sir.' There was a mumbled reply. The guard nodded. 'You can go straight in.'

The room was spacious, its oak-panelled walls lined with paintings. An OS map of the estate hung incongruously between a Monet and a Degas. Dominating the room was a mahogany desk behind which sat a man in his late fifties. In his youth Edward Braxton had been an outstanding athlete and boxer and there were still traces of what must once have been a striking physique. His shoulders were broad and his biceps strained against the silk suit. Years of good living had rounded his stomach and increased the number of his chins but his face, with its high cheek-bones and dark, brooding eyes, was that of a man used to respect.

Beside Braxton stood a man in his late twenties, of middle height with a handsome, clean-cut face and brown, curly hair. Matt Kirby was Braxton's head of security, and a more dangerous man Hamilton had never met.

'Well?' Braxton's voice was edged with irritation.

Hamilton had the impression that he'd interrupted

something important. He quickly outlined his conversation with Galbraith.

Braxton didn't conceal his annoyance. 'Couldn't this have gone in your daily report?'

'You don't understand, Mr Braxton. Galbraith's not like other coppers. Once he gets an idea into his head that's it. Christ, that's why he's ended up in this God-forsaken place. He could have been head of Glasgow CID, but he went after someone with a lot of political clout. He knows I fixed it so that the Kerr boy withdrew his statement and he's breathing down my neck.'

'And you want me to do something about it?' Braxton said. 'I hired you to sort out any troubles with the local police. Now you're getting into a panic the first time I ask you to take care of something.'

Kirby spoke for the first time, his voice pleasant, almost conversational. 'He may have a point, Mr Braxton. The last thing we need at the moment is an inquisitive police officer.'

Braxton ran a hand through his grey-black hair. 'Maybe you're right. Matt will ring Johnstone later and tell him to get Galbraith off your back. That suit you?'

Hamilton nodded. 'Thanks, Mr Braxton. Here's Manuel García's passport.'

A faint smile appeared on Kirby's face.

On his way back to the lift, Hamilton passed the corner where Braxton's huge personal bodyguard habitually stood. 'By the way,' he said, 'where's Atler?'

There was a barely perceptible pause before Kirby answered. 'Atler's mother died last night. He's gone back to the States to bury her.'

'That's right,' Braxton confirmed.

Surprise flickered across Hamilton's face as he left the

room, but he said nothing. It was a lie, he knew that. He'd seen Atler and Braxton set off early that morning to go shooting in the northern woods with a guest from London and since then nobody had left the estate.

Braxton looked up at Kirby. He'd been his head of security for three years and before that one of the youngest captains in Delta Force. A glittering army career, which included a Silver Star and a Purple Heart, had come to a premature end for reasons only Braxton and a handful of others knew.

'Keep an eye on him,' Braxton said.

Kirby nodded.

'Manuel won't have much use for this,' said Braxton, picking up the Mexican's passport.

Kirby fixed his superior with a stare that would have frozen alcohol. 'What in Christ's name were you playing at with Carter?'

Braxton's eyes narrowed. 'Things got out of hand. He was threatening to go to the authorities.'

'So you set that monster Atler on to him?' Kirby's tone couldn't hide his contempt.

'I didn't mean anyone should get killed . . .'

'You hired me to take care of problems like Carter. I turned him in the first place, got him to take the £250,000 to turn a blind eye while we removed the Hades container. Enough money to pay off his gambling debts and keep his two sons in that fancy private school. He was weak. I could have handled him – at least I could have made it look like an accident.'

Braxton was silent for several seconds. 'What's done is done. We begin Hades on schedule in four days' time. How are you planning to deal with this other problem?'

Kirby walked to the map. 'We think our man is somewhere

in this area.' He pointed to the north-west section of the estate. 'Billy is tracking him. All the guards, with the exception of a skeleton force here, will be deployed in a stopping line along the unfenced region. I've promised a $5000 bonus to whoever finds him. He should be dead by midday at the latest.'

'Good. Get this sonofabitch for me, Kirby.'

'I'll get him. Even armed he won't be a match for Billy.'

Kirby headed for the door. Without turning he said, 'I've still got some cleaning up to do after your escapade this morning, then I'm gonna join the boys in the woods.' He closed the door before Braxton could answer.

Alone, Braxton dropped his head into his hands. He'd seen the man kill Atler. He'd believed his bodyguard to be invincible. Now García was dead too. He remembered the Mexican displaying his prowess with a knife. He'd been good. But neither had been a match for Kirby. Kirby had to get him.

Hamilton was still standing in the corridor. Kirby ignored him and walked to the security area. As the thick metal door closed Hamilton spoke to the door sentry, Sam Weaver.

'Got a high opinion of himself, hasn't he, Sam?'

Weaver returned his stare coldly. 'How's that?'

Hamilton felt the other man's hostility and tried to charm his way out of trouble. 'Well, most of the other men are like you, Sam: older and more experienced. I would have thought Kirby was too young to command your respect.'

Weaver's eyes clouded with anger. He stood so close to Hamilton that the ex-police officer could smell garlic on the man's breath. 'Let me tell you something, buddy,' he said through clenched teeth, in a harsh New York accent. 'Captain Kirby's a good officer and a damn fine man. And something else,' he added, prodding Hamilton's chest with a thick finger. 'He don't take prisoners and he eats the wounded. Got the picture, buddy?'

Hamilton had been totally unprepared for the vehemence of the other man's reply. 'Christ, Sam, I didn't mean any disrespect.'

Weaver's lips compressed into a semblance of a smile. He gave a dismissive nod and returned to his chair.

Inside the security area Kirby spoke to the radio operator.

'How are things on the ground, Ox?'

'Fine now, Captain,' Hank Burrows replied. 'The new radios have been issued and most of the men have bivouacked for the night. The locations are marked on the map. There ain't been no sightings of our target.'

He was cleaning his pistol, a fifteen-shot 9mm Beretta, as he spoke. Kirby picked up some of the ammunition.

'What kind of ammo is this, Ox? I've never seen it before.'

Instead of a metal tip, the rounds were coated with hard plastic. Burrows looked up with pride.

'Black Rhino, made by Signature Products Corporation, Huntsville, Alabama. Not supposed to be on the market yet, but I've got sources. It doesn't have a lead ball. The plastic covers thousands of razor-sharp fragments. When you hit somebody with a Rhino they're just plain gonna die.'

Kirby nodded. 'I've heard of them. Mind if I take a clip?'

'Help yourself, Captain. I've got a few spare boxes.'

Kirby filled the clip on his own 9mm Glock. He spoke as he did so. 'I've got a job for you and Ike in London. You'll have to leave at first light tomorrow.'

'Sure thing, Captain.'

Kirby looked up for a second. 'I've still got some planning

to do. Get your reliefs up here and grab a quick meal. Tell Sam Weaver to get a relief as well. I want him to go to the bivouac area with me. I'll brief you and Ike before I go.'

Kirby picked up a red telephone marked 'Secure' and punched out a number from memory. It was swiftly answered.

'Highland Police.'

'I'd like to speak to Superintendent Johnstone, please.'

Outside the night was as black as a witch's heart. The headlights of Galbraith's Land Rover cast grotesque shadows against the phalanx of tall pines that flanked the A534 to Bannock. The road formed the eastern boundary of Braxton's estate, which covered nearly thirty square miles of prime mixed woodland.

Galbraith took a long drag on his cigarette. Hamilton's last words had hurt him. It had been a long time since he'd thought of her – one year, two months, three weeks, two days, to be exact. Anne, the only person in this world that had ever meant anything to him. He'd loved her so much, more than his career, honour, even life itself – still did for that matter. The only thing was, he'd never realized it at the time. He remembered her again, her eyes so warm and deep a man could look into them and keep falling for ever, the soft warmth of her body against his.

His father had not married until his late fifties. He remembered asking him why and his reply: nobody had felt right, until he'd met his mother. It had been that way with Anne. They had met at her father's retirement party. Galbraith had been asked to present a gift from CID and had found himself seated at the same table as her. She was so lovely he hardly dared look at her. The band played a slow tune and she asked him to dance. He protested that he didn't know how, but she smiled that wonderful smile and said, 'Of course you do.' They danced all night.

There'd been other women before, but the job had always got in the way. Anne had been different. He'd been able to relax in her company, tell her anything. But she'd left him. He closed his eyes as an echo of the pain twisted his stomach. Shaking his head, he drove the memory of her from his mind.

He pulled the cigarette from his mouth and let smoke leak slowly out of his lips. Through the blue-grey haze he watched the expanse of the Braxton estate flash by and muttered, 'Too much land for one man.'

'Pardon, sir?'

Galbraith shook himself out of his reverie, surprised that he'd spoken the words out loud.

'Too much land for one man,' he repeated, his voice rasping. 'What does one man need with all that land, eh, Constable?'

'Aye, sir. You couldn't walk across that estate in three days, though they do say the Yanks like things big. Jenny McCafferty, at the local grocer's, heard two of them say that McLeod House was being turned into some kind of hunting lodge for Braxton Industries executives, now that they're doing all that work at Dunston.'

Galbraith remembered the press reports. Braxton's company had signed a five-year contract to have spent fuel rods reprocessed at the nuclear power station neighbouring the estate.

'God knows why the government allowed that. We have enough problems getting rid of our own nuclear waste without importing it from America.'

'That's as maybe, sir, but it has been very good for business.

25

Why, Jenny says her takings have trebled in the three months that the Braxton people have been here.'

A sign flashed up in front of them: 'Welcome To The Town Of Bannock'. In fact it was little more than a large village, with one main street around which a haphazard collection of homes, pubs and two churches sprawled in a loose half-mile circle.

Three towns just like it and nearly a hundred square miles of trees, hills and moors were Galbraith's patch. He'd applied for the vacant Chief Inspector's job just six months ago. His outstanding CID record had ensured he got it. That, and the fact that he was the only applicant. Both he and the examining board knew his career with the Strathclyde Police was effectively over and this was about all there was for him.

The main street was deserted as the Land Rover pulled up outside a picturesque grey-stone, two-storey building. Every time Galbraith saw the blue lantern he felt he'd taken a step back fifty years.

He had twelve uniformed officers and four CID men working, in three shifts, to cover an area the size of some English counties. Stepping into the hallway, he found his entire evening shift – four men – behind the old wooden front desk. Each seemed to be occupied. Galbraith nodded towards one of his sergeants. Angus Mackenzie probably had the worst arrest record of any officer in the history of policing – two men in nearly twenty-five years – but nothing happened in a fifty-mile radius without him knowing about it. His round, florid face beamed a welcome.

'Evening, Mr Galbraith.'

'Angus, why the hell are . . .?'

'Mr Galbraith,' Angus interrupted hurriedly, 'you have a visitor.'

Seated on the wooden bench that ran the length of the opposite wall was one of the most attractive women he'd ever seen. She stood to greet him. Perhaps five foot eight tall, she had raven-black, shoulder-length hair and eyes of a strikingly deep green that held intelligence, warmth and promise.

She extended her hand. 'My name is Reynolds, Charlotte Reynolds. I've been waiting to see you, Chief Inspector.' Her voice was soft, educated, Lowland Scots, yet carried the length of the room. Galbraith accepted her surprisingly strong grip and tried not to lose himself in those eyes.

'Angus, I think it's time the evening shift began its patrols,' he said softly.

'Aye, sir.' Behind the big sergeant the three younger men began to move quickly towards the exits. Galbraith suppressed a smile. 'Would you come with me, Miss Reynolds. These gentlemen have work to do.'

When they were seated in his office, he offered his guest tea, which she refused. He studied her across his desk. She wore a dark business suit over a cream silk blouse. He looked at her hands. They too were beautiful despite the ridges of hard skin between the thumb and forefinger on her right hand. He'd seen those before. He looked up, smiling.

'So, Miss Reynolds, what can I do for you?'

The young woman handed over a purple plastic folder inside which was an ID card that stated: 'Charlotte Reynolds, National Rivers Authority'. There were various contact numbers and Galbraith jotted them down out of habit.

'The NRA has been informed that some building work is starting on the Braxton estate within the next two to three days.'

'So I believe. I'm told they're building a hunting lodge

for company employees. Braxton's obtained the appropriate planning permissions.'

'Yes, I'm sure. We opposed the building, unsuccessfully. I'm going to be here for a few weeks checking the local rivers, making sure there's no build-up in pollution levels. I didn't want you getting reports of a strange woman loitering in the woods.'

They both laughed.

Charlotte continued. 'The estate feeds some of the best salmon rivers in Scotland. Do you know when the work is beginning?'

Never, Galbraith was thinking, had he been interrogated so charmingly. He glanced again at his guest's jacket. It was clearly hand-made, yet one of the lapels hung fractionally lower than the other. He'd seen that before as well. 'I've been told to expect some heavy lorries going through the town centre in three days. Are you going to be inspecting the estate itself, Miss Reynolds?'

'I'd love to, but unfortunately we haven't been able to get permission. Mr Braxton certainly likes his security.'

'Yes, forty specially trained guards, a double wire fence round the perimeter and the most modern electronic surveillance system on the market. That's security all right.'

'Is the entire estate fenced?'

'Not yet. There's an unfenced section to the north, bordering the Melville Hills. It's about four miles long. Why do you ask?' Galbraith's eyes narrowed slightly, but his smile broadened.

'Just curiosity.'

'I wouldn't advise you to go on the estate uninvited. Those guards of Braxton's are a bad bunch; put three local lads in hospital just the other month.'

'I've no intention of coming up against them, I assure you.' Charlotte stood and he handed back her folder.

'What are you really doing here, Miss Reynolds?' he asked.

'I've told you,' she replied evenly, 'I'm here to test some river water. You can check my credentials.'

'I intend to.'

She held his gaze for several seconds, then headed for the door. 'I'll be seeing you, Chief Inspector.'

Galbraith spoke to the empty room. 'I'm sure of it, Miss Reynolds, I'm sure of it.'

3

Outside the police station Charlotte checked her watch. Swiftly she walked the short distance to one of Bannock's three public telephones. From her jacket pocket she produced a small black book on the inside page of which was a list of phone numbers. She chose one and dialled. In a phone box in London a man in his late fifties picked up the receiver after the third ring.

'Hello.'

'It's Charlotte.'

'How are things?'

Charlotte smiled. 'Things are very bad.' It was a simple code. If she'd said things were good, it would have warned her superior that she was speaking under pressure.

'What have you to report?'

'I've made contact with the local Chief Inspector. He's everything his personal file said he was. He's already suspicious of me.'

'We expected that.'

'Any word from Carter?'

'Nothing. His office say he's on annual leave.'

'OK. I'm staying at the Marquis of Montrose if you need to reach me in a hurry.'

'Be careful, Charlotte. We still don't know exactly what

we're up against, and my position here is less than secure.'

'I understand.'

The phone went dead. Charlotte replaced the handset and stared across the empty street.

The forest was a quiet place even by day and during darkness only the occasional call of a hunting owl disturbed its peace. Fraser slept in the foetal position, his hands and legs grasped round the rifle. His sleep was light and troubled. Half-recognized faces swam before him. He tried to study them, only to watch them disappear.

He saw himself outside a terraced house in a nameless street. He knew he was in danger. There were men inside who wanted to kill him and in his ear a commanding voice was asking how many targets there were.

'Four,' he answered.

A hand grasped his shoulder from behind. He felt the cool touch of a revolver barrel against his neck.

'Got you, you Brit bastard!' a voice spat in a staccato accent he could barely understand.

He was flung against a chain-link fence, the cold metal branding his face. A searching hand passed urgently over his body. There was a call for help. Forcing his head round he saw a man coming towards him, carrying a rifle. He was young, barely out of his teens, but his face was aged with a feral hatred. Their eyes met and he saw something else — anticipation. The man behind him was reaching down to search his legs. The pressure of the barrel on his neck eased slightly. He pivoted on his right heel, the natural turn of his body driving his elbow into the bending man's face. He gave a silent scream of agony as the man's nose broke under the impact.

The other man brought up his rifle. Now fear made him once again appear young. Seemingly without effort, Fraser pulled his own pistol from the front of his waistband. He fired. The man's mouth erupted in a gout of blood. Behind him he heard the first man groping for his fallen revolver. Fraser turned, almost in slow motion, and shot him as well. Then he started to run.

There was a babble of angry voices. His legs were leaden, his lungs craved air. The voices and shouts got louder. They were gaining on him . . .

He woke. There was no fuzzy transition from sleep to wakefulness. He sat up in the darkness, the dream still vivid in his mind. Despite the cold he was covered in a film of sweat. He pulled Manuel's jacket tight around him like a blanket. He peered at his watch: just before ten. He had been asleep for nearly four hours.

He thought about his dreams, the woman who had called to him, the men he'd killed. He lay down again. Drifting across the still night air came the screech of a hunting owl. Then he heard the distinctive beating of wings; the hunter had made its kill. He sympathized with the quarry; he knew exactly how it felt. He closed his eyes, and in seconds he was asleep.

Five miles to the north a Range Rover bumped its way along a twisting track. A man stepped into its path, a torch in one hand, an Armalite AR18 rifle in the other. Recognizing the driver, he sprang to attention.

'Good evening, Captain Kirby.'

'Evening, George. Where's the bivouac area?'

'About twenty yards to your left, Captain.'

Sam Weaver climbed out to join him.

'Sam, you and George go tell the boys I'm here. Briefing in twenty minutes.'

'Yessir.'

Alone, Kirby fished inside his hunting jacket for a hand-rolled Havana cigar. They were smuggled to him in batches of two hundred by a friend in the Marine Corps stationed in Guantanamo Bay. He limited himself to two a day. Cuba — he'd served there once for six months. He was eighteen at the time, a fierce protector of justice and truth. Then came Grenada, where he'd won his Silver Star by knocking out two machine-gun posts after his platoon leader had been killed. The medal had been his ticket to officer school, where he finished third in his class. Finally came his selection for Delta Force.

And all of it ended in Mogadishu, Somalia, on a blistering afternoon, when a horde of Somali gunmen had ambushed a Marine convoy.

He was in the operations room when the call came in: 'Hell, they're everywhere.' The sounds of explosions and automatic-rifle fire could be heard clearly above the second lieutenant's high-pitched voice, tinged with the first onslaught of panic.

'Can you see the helicopter? It should be above you now.' The general in charge of the operations room was calm and authoritative.

Some of the confidence rubbed off on the lieutenant. When he answered, his voice was firm. 'Yes sir, I can see him now.'

'Good. Now listen, boy. When he's directly overhead I want you to throw smoke, understand?'

'Yes, sir, I've got it. Oh my God, he's hit. The copter's coming down.' There was a deafening explosion, then silence.

The general pressed the relay switch. 'Charlie Twelve, come in. Over.' He tried four more times, to no avail, then put down the transmitter.

'Captain Kirby, who do you have available?'

'Two sergeants and me, sir. The rest are already in action.'

The general rubbed the bottom half of his face with an open hand. 'I need some eyes and ears on the ground, Captain. It's a volunteer mission only.'

Kirby looked at his two sergeants standing in the op room's doorway. They grinned back at him. 'No problem about that, General.'

'Good.' The general clapped him on the shoulder, then spoke quickly. 'You know the situation. The convoy is spread out over a half-mile. I need to know enemy strength and the whereabouts of the survivors before I bring in the gunships. Take my bird. It's fuelled and ready. Drop your two sergeants with radios. You are not, repeat not, to go with your men, Captain. I want you in the air, telling me what's going on. Got that?'

'Loud and clear, sir.'

'Move out — and good luck.'

Minutes later they were speeding towards the ambush point. There were burning trucks and dead bodies everywhere, some American, dozens of Somalis. He spotted the downed helicopter. Around it were a group of men still firing at an enemy he couldn't see. He turned to the sergeants. 'Pete, Jimmy, keep in contact at all times. I want to bring in an air strike ASAP. OK?'

Rounds started to hit the helicopter. The pilot cursed, but the three Special Forces men ignored him.

They went down fast. The pilot knew his business. Pete and Jimmy jumped out eight feet from the ground. The pilot throttled back and they climbed rapidly. The air around them filled with lead.

Almost immediately Pete came on the air. 'It's real messy down here, Captain. At least eight dead, four more wounded. The pilot is one of them. The wounded guys are almost out of ammo.'

'Roger that, Pete. What about the enemy?'

'They're concentrated about fifty yards to my left. I'm going to fire some tracer toward them. Watch out.'

Five red pinpricks of light streamed out from the convoy. Kirby plotted a grid reference.

'Got that, Pete. I'll get an air strike in.'

'Roger. Those tracer really got their attention. The firing is real heavy now. Holy Mother of God.'

A horde of Somali gunmen appeared from the ramshackle huts to the convoy's left, most armed with Soviet Kalashnikov assault rifles.

Kirby turned to the pilot. 'Take us down.'

'Don't be stupid, Captain – there's nothing we can do.'

'I said take us down.'

'No, it's suicide. Look.'

Below them the sky was filled with tracer and the explosions of rocket-propelled grenades.

'Captain.' It was Pete, struggling to keep his weak voice coherent. 'Jimmy's dead. I'm hit. Tell my father, tell him . . .'

He watched helplessly as the Somalis swarmed over the trucks. The pilot pressed a switch on his dashboard: the on-board video recorded the scene. Kirby watched in cold fury. Jimmy's body was tied to the back of a truck and driven round in circles. Pete was dismembered and his head raised high on a pole. By the time the Apache attack helicopters arrived most of the gunmen had vanished.

Three months later they were pulling out like thieves in the night. But Kirby had used those months well. From the helicopter's video he'd obtained photographs of the killers and from interrogations with friendly Somalis he'd identified the men who'd killed his sergeants. He handpicked his squad, Hank Burrows, Ike Phillips and Manuel García among them, and slipped out of the

UN compound in the early-morning darkness. In the next two hours he located and executed all ten men. They saved the one who'd held Pete's head up on that damn pole for last.

The burning cigar scorched Kirby's fingers and brought him back to the present. His military career had ended that day: the army didn't like executioners. Although his previous record and decorations had saved him from a court martial the life he loved had gone.

Now he was chasing some poor limey bastard through a Scottish wood. He hoped Billy would kill him quickly. Billy had been recruited from a crack Ranger battalion and had proved to be a good soldier but inclined to cruelty beyond belief if left unsupervised.

Before first light the wood came alive. As if at some pre-set signal dozens of birds broke into song. Fraser woke at once and rose swiftly. It was cold. He stamped his feet as he pulled on the jacket. The thought uppermost in his mind, despite his predicament, was that he could murder a cup of tea. 'Give a man a mug of hot tea, a fresh pair of socks and a letter from home and he's good for another fifty miles.' He couldn't remember who had given him that particular piece of advice.

Fingers of light began to steal through the trees as the sun began its slow climb over the eastern horizon. He saw the hills he'd been heading for, closer now but still a good fifteen miles away. Picking up the AK47, he was about to set off towards them when a thought stopped him in his tracks. He hadn't checked it.

He knelt and watched in fascination as his hands seemed to move of their own volition, removing the banana-shaped magazine and inserting a thumb to test if it was fully loaded. The rounds gave way, telling him that the magazine was

36

loaded with twenty-eight rather than its maximum thirty, probably to stop the spring from becoming weak. After clicking the big side lever off the 'safe' position, he tilted the compact rifle and cocked it. A glittering brass round was ejected on to the forest floor. He picked it up. Words tumbled through his mind: 7.62 short, maximum effective range 150 yards, stopping power like a brick through a glass window, best all-round assault rifle ever produced, needs very little maintenance or training, superb weapon for indigenous troops, standard issue of most East European armies, over twenty-five million produced. He inserted the round back into the magazine, replaced it on the rifle and cocked it again. As he set off he realized that he understood every word.

He moved swiftly for half an hour, putting distance between himself and his sleeping place. Hunger gnawed at his belly again. Ahead of him he heard the sound of running water and headed for it. Ten minutes later he found a deep, fast-flowing stream, about six feet wide, probably a tributary of the river he'd nearly died in the day before. He walked along the bank until he found the right place, a tree over-hanging a bend where the water slowed.

Stripping off his belt, he carefully took out a few yards of nylon fishing line and a hook. He tied the hook on and cut off the few inches of excess line close to the knot. This he used to tie on a dry twig, parallel to the line and a couple of feet above the hook. He walked a little way along the bank, inspecting the trees, until he spotted what he was looking for: a rotting tree. Pulling away the crumbling bark, he scooped out a handful of beetles and made his way back to his fishing place. There he baited his hook with a couple of the fattest insects.

Keeping well back from the water, in the shadow of the

tree, he threw a few of the remaining beetles into the far side of the stream. Fish rose to take them almost immediately, before they sank, making rings on the surface as they sucked them in. Fraser then swung the baited line out into the same stretch of water.

The twig float dipped at once and he pulled sharply on the line. Nothing. Too slow. He pulled in, rebaited the hook and cast out again. A ripple broke the surface and he felt another vigorous tug. This time he connected with a brown trout of about a pound. After pulling it in smartly and removing the hook from its mouth he cut its throat to allow it to bleed. Then he hooked some more beetles and threw the line out again. Three minutes later he'd landed another trout, slightly smaller than the first.

After cutting off the heads and tails of his catch, he slit their bellies and scraped out their innards. He diced the gutted fish, scales and all. After putting the flesh in the steel mug from the bottom of his water bottle, he suspended the vessel over a small fire next to the base of a tree, which would hide the fire and disperse the smoke. Boiling the fish would not only retain all its goodness but also prevent the aroma carrying very far.

While his meal cooked he scavenged near by. On a tree he found a number of tawny, brown-speckled caps of the honey fungus. After picking enough, he returned to his simmering stew and sliced them into it.

When the fish was tender he removed the mug from the heat and let it cool for a few minutes before draining every last drop of the nutritious fluid. He burped satisfyingly as he washed out the mug in the stream and refilled his water bottles. So far the forest had provided a plentiful supply of food, and he hoped it would last. He checked his watch. He'd stopped beside the stream for nearly half an hour – it was time to put some distance between himself and the hunters he knew would be on his trail. He set off at a brisk pace.

In the next three hours he covered less than five miles. The country was all hidden dips and rises. The undergrowth became thicker, forcing him several times to make wide detours round impassable stretches. Occasionally he crossed a track. He was wary at such times, knowing the men who were after him would use them to move faster than he could. It was when he stopped for a water break just before noon that he felt his first premonition. He was on top of a small rise. He studied the ground he'd covered. Could a man track him through this terrain? It seemed unlikely, yet the feeling wouldn't go away. A hundred yards behind him a bird suddenly flew into the air. He wasted no more time in speculation.

'If a fight is inevitable, choose the ground.' Fifty yards further on he found it: a long, flat stretch, with little cover to the left and thick bushes to the right. He walked in a nearly straight line for thirty yards, then jumped to the right. Moving into the thick cover a good five yards, he backtracked to where he'd started his straight walk. Settling down with a thick tree to his left, he set the rifle down two clicks, for single shots – the first click was for automatic fire – and waited in ambush on his own tracks.

Billy was enjoying himself: it had been a long time since he'd tracked a man. He'd been taught to track by his father, like his father before him, all the way back to when his forebears roamed the country from the Canadian border to the Florida coast. It was an age-old skill: from the depth of an animal's imprint you could gauge its age and height; from the way it spread its legs when it urinated, you'd know its sex. Under his father's patient guidance, the ground became an open book.

Tracking a human was different. Following a man entailed knowing as much about psychology as signs, Billy's father had always told him. Animals always wandered this way and that in search of food or shade, but men took a more direct route – unless they were lost. Men were also lazy, his father had been at great pains to remind him; they nearly always took the easiest path. When tracking a man, the hunter should always look ahead for the route his quarry would take and only look down occasionally to confirm the track. In this way he would not only stay on the track but also gain ground quickly on his prey.

The last time Kirby had sent him after a man was five years ago, in Central America. They had been part of a training team, organized to instruct a right-wing guerrilla group. A government agent had joined them but then deserted with vital information. The locals had said it was impossible to track a man through the impenetrable jungles and swamps that surrounded the camp. But Billy Red Bear had caught and killed him inside twenty-four hours. After that there were no more deserters. Now Kirby had sent him to hunt a man again and it felt good.

Billy had realized quickly that Fraser was heading for the Melville Hills and he'd been able to gain on him steadily. He knew a lot about the man he would kill. His height from his stride pattern, his weight from the depth of track. Billy knew also that he was fit and that he was alert: he stopped every fifty yards to look behind and to the sides of his track. He knew he carried his rifle in both hands when he moved, even when going up steep ground, and kept it near him when he stopped. That spoke of training.

The Indian had found where the man had slept overnight. He'd spotted the remains of his two meals: this man was no stranger to the woods. Of more concern to him were the signs that Fraser had rested the butt of the AK47 on the ground to eject the round in its breech. Billy had recognized the particular indentation in the butt where the oil bottle for the weapon was stored. Kirby was right. This guy was no beginner: he'd had the sense to check his rifle before moving.

Billy found his track easily enough: he was still heading towards the Melvilles, moving cautiously. He set out after him at a mile-eating lope, knowing that before midday he'd catch up with him. The stride pattern remained unaltered, and the tracks were getting fresher.

Billy reached the top of a small rise and noticed where the man had stopped again to look behind him. A freshly scraped scar on a moss-covered rock showed where his feet had turned in a full circle. The tracks were very fresh now, less than half an hour old. He pressed on, the thrill of the hunt rising within him.

The track had suddenly veered away from the heading to the distant hills. The hunter paused and stood, still as the trees around him. There was a clear route across to the next valley, yet the man had moved off to the right. Why? He studied the tracks more intently. They were as plain as at any time, but there was something wrong, something different. The stride pattern had altered, the steps were shorter, more deliberate.

He glanced to his left without moving his head. Open ground, no cover, a good place for an ambush. Thought and action were as one. He twisted quickly to his right, bringing up his Heckler & Koch G3 rifle in a smooth arc. Billy's swift

41

reaction caught Fraser by surprise. For seconds they observed one another. The Apache fired first.

Billy's bullet missed him by a few millimetres. As it broke the sound barrier above Fraser's head he fired twice in quick succession, a double tap aimed at the centre of the man in front of him. Instinctively he knew that his rounds had hit. Billy flew backwards, the long German rifle falling from his hand.

Fraser waited a full minute before leaving cover, then moved swiftly to his left. He advanced on the downed man, never shifting his aim. The hunter was dying. One round had pierced the left lung, the other slashed through the sternum, causing massive internal bleeding. The dark eyes observed him with undisguised malevolence. The man tried to speak. Bright, frothy blood sprayed from his lips. 'How did you know I was tracking you?' The words were little more than a croak.

Fraser answered slowly. 'I didn't. I just felt something was wrong.'

The dying man's eyes clouded. He stared at Fraser and struggled to ask one final question. 'Who are you?' He coughed twice, spraying more of the bright red blood over his chest, then gave a deep sigh and was still.

In reply, Fraser spoke to his audience of trees. 'I only wish I knew,' he said softly. He knelt and rifled through the dead man's pockets. He pulled out food and ammunition; the latter he discarded as it was incompatible with his own rifle. Then he found a compass and a map, which he studied with interest. 'Well, well, I'm in bonny Scotland. That's a start at least.' Seconds later he was on the move again.

When Billy hadn't reported in, Kirby had taken a bearing on

the sound of the gunfire. They had walked towards it through most of the afternoon, expecting at any moment to come face to face with their comrade. As the afternoon wore on Kirby became more agitated.

Frank sensed his unease. 'Maybe he was lucky enough to get a shot off before Billy killed him.'

Kirby didn't answer.

Frank felt compelled to speak again. 'Or maybe Billy only wounded him and he holed up. Billy could be just sitting waiting for him to die.'

Kirby threw him a withering glance and Frank took his cue to be quiet.

A mile further on Leo Gunn held up a hand. All three men froze. Ahead of them on open ground lay a twisted body. Kirby took a step to his right and jerked his head. Gunn and Frank moved out to search the area, moving in a loose circle of about twenty yards around the body. Each of them had his rifle in his shoulder, moving the barrel from right to left as he searched for a target.

Kirby knelt on one knee, his rifle covering them until they gave him the thumbs up to indicate that the area was clear. Only then did they approach the body. Kirby turned it over with the toecap of his boot, not really surprised to find that it was Billy. He bent down to inspect the body, then straightened, shaking his head. Billy had been one of his best men, one of his very best. He'd have backed him against anybody, except himself and Leo Gunn. Kirby looked into Gunn's impassive features.

Both men had the same question on their mind, but it was Kirby who voiced it. 'Who the hell is this guy?'

4

Fraser tried desperately to cover his tracks after the fire-fight with the Indian. He doubled back on his own spoor several times and ran backwards along a fallen tree. A sheen of sweat covered his face. Just before sunset, after dog-legging his own trail yet again, he lay up and watched till darkness closed in. Only then did he relax.

After slipping off his belt, which was now chafing his waist, he took out the food – dried meat and dried fruit – taken from his assailant and munched it slowly, considering his next move. Finding the map had been a bonus. The security fence he had brushed up against that morning was marked with double red lines. Just beyond where the lines ended, a range of hills called the Melvilles began. He decided his best bet was to try to reach the unfenced area.

He finished his frugal meal, checked both his weapons, then laid the short assault rifle beside him. The Browning automatic he kept in his hand; if he was disturbed during the night it would be swifter to use and had a wider arc of fire. He rolled up in his heavy jacket to sleep.

A blunt pain coursed through his head. He tried to remember the faces of the men he'd killed, but the more he tried to concentrate the less sure he was of the chronology of events. Did they actually happen or were they dreams too?

He tried to focus on his encounter with the Indian. Flashing dots appeared before his eyes and a dull ringing sounded in his ears. He shook his head violently. The pain worsened and the ringing became louder. A surge of nausea overcame him, his jaw locked and he retched. He closed his eyes, lay still and forced himself to take several deep breaths. Slowly the pain subsided. He massaged his sweat-covered brow. He was exhausted by the effort to remember.

He cushioned his head on a pillow of leaves. As his eyes closed, a woman's soft voice drifted through his thoughts: 'You didn't start it, they did, so hell mend them.' Who had said that to him and why? He knew if he tried to find the answer the pain would return and besides he was so tired and the leaves that were his pillow were so soft. The darkness enfolded him, but his sleep was not peaceful. He tossed and turned and suddenly called out a name.

The café was filled to capacity with workers from the nearby building sites. An old man, his face worn by time but showing pride in the two rows of medal ribbons he had pinned on his chest, shuffled to the counter. He wore an ancient navy-blue blazer, its breast pocket adorned with the double-winged emblem of the Parachute Regiment, and a single red poppy in his buttonhole. Beside him, one of a group of youths glanced first at the medals and then at the badge. 'Look lads, a bloody hero.' The accent was pure Bogside.

'What's your trouble, son?' asked the old man, his voice trembling slightly.

'I'm not your son,' the youth snarled. Muscles rippled beneath the thin T-shirt as a finger the size of a pork sausage poked at the old man's chest. 'How many of those did you get for gunning down innocent women and children in Derry?'

'I've never been to Ireland. I fought in the War.'

'Paras are murdering scum. You lot killed my cousin.' He seized the older man's lapels and propelled him backwards towards his two companions.

'Looks like the hero's drunk,' he sneered. 'Can't hold your drink, man.'

'Leave him alone.'

The woman's blue eyes sparkled with fury. Her white coat could not disguise the contours of her body as she stood, hands on hips, in front of the bullying youth. 'You should be ashamed of yourself. He's an old man. He's . . .'

'He's a Para,' the youth said with disdain. He pushed his red face closer to hers.

One of the others moved behind her and carved out her figure with his hands. The first youth leered. 'But we don't want to be arguing now, do we?' He raised his calloused hand towards her face. She snapped her head back in disgust and the youth behind her caught her shoulders.

'Sure, I don't think she likes you, Gerry.'

'Leave the lady alone,' he heard himself say from his corner seat.

They turned towards him. 'Stay out of this if you know what's good for you.'

'I've never known what's good for me.' The voice echoed in his head.

The youth with his hands on the woman's shoulders pushed her to one side. 'Well, maybe I can show you.'

He watched the youth come towards him, throwing a sweeping haymaker as he advanced. Stepping to his left, he avoided the blow with ease, then brought up his right foot and stamped viciously on the side of the youth's knee, collapsing his leg. He drove his elbow into the exposed side of the kneeling man's head

46

as he moved towards Gerry. With a snarl of anger Gerry launched a kick at him. He caught the leg effortlessly, then punched him in the groin. Pain distorted Gerry's face as he collapsed. The third youth held both hands up in supplication. Ignoring him, he helped the old soldier to his feet.

'Are you OK?'

'Fine, son, just fine. I could have done with you in '44 at Arnhem Bridge.'

He laughed. The girl was by his side. 'I'm sorry about the trouble.'

She looked at the fallen youths. 'They started it and "hell mend them", as my father used to say. But I suppose now I'll have to put them back together. My name's Lindsey . . .'

'My name's . . .' The mist closed in around his mind. He tried to reach through it. 'No. My name's . . .'

He sat up. The forest was quiet around him. He clasped his head in his hands, fighting to clear the uncertainty and pain. He had a sense of loss that he couldn't begin to understand. Her face haunted him. He shivered as he lay down again, despite being wrapped in his jacket. This time sleep eluded him.

Brian Hamilton liked luxury; liked it and pursued it. His easy-going good looks and 'love me, please' smile had always hidden a deep, almost pathological, desire to acquire the wealth and status he felt should have been his by right. His efforts to achieve this had started early: as a police officer in Glasgow CID he'd taken pay-offs from illegal gambling dens in return for warnings about raids or investigations. His underworld contacts fed him a steady flow of low-grade information that was enough for him to keep up a good arrest and clear-up record and impress his superiors.

Glasgow's exploding drug culture of the early eighties provided the best opportunity for enrichment and Hamilton wasn't slow to recognize the fact. He became the inside man for Arthur Thompson, the city's criminal Godfather, and before long, he was earning nearly three times his police salary. It couldn't last. Thompson's unexpected death led to press stories of police involvement. Hamilton resigned, one step ahead of an internal corruption probe.

McLeod House epitomized the luxury he'd always craved. His spacious, oak-panelled room was furnished with a four-poster bed big enough to lose several people in. But, despite the comfort of his surroundings, Hamilton couldn't relax. He tossed aside the tangled mass of linen sheets and reached for a cigarette.

This whole set-up had seemed so sweet: £50,000 a year to keep the locals happy and a senior police officer already in Braxton's pocket. Then Galbraith had arrived and Hamilton wanted to know why. There was something going on here, something big. He could see it in the actions of the Americans and sense it when conversations suddenly stopped as he got close enough to hear.

He rubbed his eyes and strolled towards the window. He glanced out, then took a quick step back. Kirby was outside and two vehicles were approaching. The leading one was a Braxton Range Rover, the other a civilian car which Hamilton recognized as the Jaguar XJ6 that yesterday's guest had been driving. Hank Burrows and Ike Phillips emerged from the vehicles and after a few words both men drove off, leaving the security chief alone.

'What in hell's going on here?' he said softly. Fixing a simple grievous bodily harm assault was one thing, but he didn't want to be caught up in events. He had no doubts about the power that Braxton wielded and what Kirby might do to him if he knew what was going through his mind. He must take steps to protect himself. Galbraith might be the key. Although the man hated Hamilton for more than one good reason, he was first and foremost a dedicated police officer. Yes, Galbraith might very well be the answer. As the morning light filtered through his window he came to a decision.

He swiftly shaved and dressed. Keeping to his normal routine, he sauntered down the carved staircase to the ground floor. With the exception of Braxton and Kirby, the whole household ate in the dining hall, but when he got there he found only one other person at table: Leo Gunn, the black man, working his way through a stack of eggs, bacon and pancakes. Hamilton helped himself to some toast and tea and sat next to him, giving him his most engaging smile. 'I'll never get used to the amount of food you Americans put away in the morning.'

Gunn ignored the comment and continued shovelling food into his mouth. Hamilton had expected no less: the black man was to polite conversation what Adolf Hitler was to race relations. He glanced round the empty room. 'Boys still out in the woods playing soldiers?' he asked.

'The men are still out on a security exercise and will be for at least two more days.' The voice came from behind him. He looked round to see Kirby standing by the door. The security chief got himself some coffee and sat opposite him. The penetrating stare of the smaller man unnerved Hamilton, but he steadied himself and managed a smile.

'I'm going into town,' he said. 'Is there anything I can get for you?'

Kirby ignored the last part of the question. 'Why?'

'My wife Anne's coming up for the day. We're having lunch together.'

Kirby studied him over the rim of his cup. 'This isn't good timing, Brian. We're short-handed around here right now. There may be trouble with the new hunting lodge and there's still this assault business to clear up.'

'It's only a couple of hours, Matt, and she's coming all the way from Glasgow.'

'You know what Mr Braxton prizes more than anything else in this world?'

Hamilton shook his head.

'Loyalty. You're not gonna disappoint us, are you, Brian?'

The words, so softly spoken, chilled Hamilton's soul. 'I'm just going to see my wife, Matt.' Even to himself his voice sounded weak. 'Besides, I'm just a PR man. I'm not involved with anything that's going on round here.' Hamilton knew at once that he'd made a mistake.

Kirby's head tilted slightly to one side as he put down his cup and steepled his hands on the table in front of him. 'What makes you think something is going on?'

Silence hung between them. Hamilton felt his stomach clench, making it hard for him to breathe. He looked sideways to see Gunn set down his cutlery and watch him with unblinking intensity. The man's muscular weight caused the chair to creak. In his excited state, it sounded to Hamilton like a pistol shot, and he flinched involuntarily.

'Bit jumpy, aren't we, old friend?' said Kirby, then reached across and picked the last slice of toast from Hamilton's plate and bit into it, studying him intently.

Hamilton looked from one man to the other. Several times he tried to speak, but his mouth was too dry.

Kirby suddenly smiled. 'You're right, of course: we can

do without you for the day. How's the little lady getting to Bannock?'

Relief coursed through Hamilton's body. He forced himself to smile. 'She's coming up by train.'

'I can't spare a vehicle for the whole day, but I'll get one of the boys to drop you off and pick you up at that pub in town. OK?'

'Fine, Matt, as long as it's no trouble.'

'None at all.' The security chief stood abruptly. 'I'll just go and arrange the transport. You be ready to leave in about fifteen minutes.'

Without waiting for a reply, Kirby walked briskly to the control room, still chewing Hamilton's toast. The radio operator turned as he entered.

'Get three of the boys up here – I've got a rush job for them.' He paced the small operations room until the men arrived, then took only a few minutes to brief them. Two of them left quickly and the third followed him back to the dining hall.

'Jackson will drive you into town,' he told Hamilton. 'He's got some business to take care of for the boss.'

Hamilton skirted the refectory table and followed Kirby and Jackson to the entrance.

'Now you be sure you're back here before dark. I know what you married men get up to when you haven't seen your wives for a while.' Kirby clapped Hamilton's back and closed the door before he could reply. He then took the lift, deep in thought, to Braxton's apartment on the top floor. On arriving there he nodded to the guard, knocked and entered in response to Braxton's gruff reply.

The tycoon's eyes were bloodshot, his face lined. A breakfast tray lay untouched near his desk.

'Any news?'

'None. I've got two four-man patrols trying to cut his track, but so far no luck.'

'Three of our men dead,' Braxton said.

'Yes, two more and our boy will qualify for automatic American citizenship.'

'I don't need jokes, I need results. We have less than three days before the operation begins. I want this man found before then. What's your next move?'

'He's trying to reach the unfenced sector to the north. The wood stops here.' Kirby pointed to the Ordnance Survey map. 'He then has two hundred yards of open ground before he can reach the Melville Hills. If my patrols don't get him this afternoon, it's my bet he'll lie up and try and cross it sometime tonight. That will be our best time to nail him.'

Braxton stared at the map. 'Fine,' he said eventually. 'But whatever happens, we must go ahead on schedule.'

'Roger that, Mr Braxton.'

Kirby walked towards the door, then stopped and turned almost as an afterthought.

'By the way, I think you were right about Hamilton. I may have to let him go.'

'Really?'

'Yes. I'll know for sure in a few hours.'

'Do whatever you have to.'

Kirby nodded and left.

Fraser had risen at first light and covered a mile before he stopped to strip the rifle. First he removed the magazine, then depressed the catch at the rear of the covering slide and lifted it off to reveal the working parts. He pulled them out, ejecting the 7.62mm short round from the barrel. The barrel was filthy, so he improvised a pull-through from a length of fishing line weighted with a sinker and cleaned the weapon thoroughly. He put it together again quickly, hand-feeding the round into the chamber to avoid noise. His hands seemed to move of their own volition, knowing exactly where each piece should go. He then checked the Browning. The single-action automatic was in better condition. Having emptied the magazine, he counted the rounds: only ten, less than its twelve-round maximum. Then, after reassembling the pistol, he ate.

Ever since he'd woken that morning his thoughts had been dominated by her face and by an overwhelming sense of loss. Why was this the only thing he could remember clearly? Why should she arouse so much emotion in him? The pain of his head wound became worse as he tried to concentrate. Suddenly he saw her. Saw her in these woods, so clearly that he stood up, his rifle clattering nosily at his feet. He looked around but as fast as the vision had come it disappeared. He sat down abruptly and cradled his head in his hands. He felt a wave of exhaustion sweep over him that had nothing to do with physical exertion. The more he tried to concentrate the less he could fathom these fragmented thoughts and images. He took deep breaths and forced himself to concentrate on staying alive. Picking up his fallen rifle, he considered how the men were hunting him, not why. The answer to that would come later.

A rifle bullet smashed into the tree next to his head. There was no time for fear, only instinct. Snatching the AK47, he rolled to his left, just avoiding a volley of shots. He cursed himself – he'd been caught daydreaming. More bullets crashed into the trees around him, narrowly missing his prone body. He counted least four weapons. He began to roll, the rifle clutched tightly to his chest, in an attempt to get out of the area where the fire was concentrated. Bullets cracked and whined around him. He tumbled into a long, straight drainage channel cut by foresters. It was about three feet deep, half-filled with black water and as welcome as a red carpet to a whore's bedroom. He scrambled along it frantically, trying to keep below its rim.

The volley had slackened, to be replaced by systematic short bursts and unintelligible shouts. He knew his attackers were skirmishing towards his last position. If they went through and found the trench he'd be in big trouble. He inched his head cautiously over the edge of the water channel. They were about twenty yards from him, searching the area where he'd stopped to eat. Keeping flat, he crawled out of the trench and burrowed into thick cover. He brought the rifle up, sighted and fired two quick shots. Quickly he rolled to the left, fired two more, then rolled right, squirmed backwards four or five feet, got into a low crouch and ran like all the demons in hell were on his heels. Behind him he could hear cries of anger and pain.

It took the patrol an hour to make their way to the nearest track, where Kirby was waiting for them. Their leader was the big New Yorker, Sam Weaver. He put down the man he was carrying and staggered over to the security chief.

'We heard him drop his rifle and patrolled toward him. He was sitting on a tree when the point man opened fire,' Weaver said, shaking his head in frustration. 'We thought we had him, Mr Kirby, but he reacted like greased lightning. Somehow he got out of the killing zone and flanked us.' He looked back at the two groaning men behind him. 'He fired four shots in about three seconds and hit two of us with three rounds. This sonofabitch is good.'

Kirby lit a cigar. It was his third that morning. The bastard was turning him into an addict. 'How badly hurt are your men?'

'Mike's got a shoulder wound. Jim's hit in both legs. They'll live, but they're gonna be out of action for at least three months.'

'Get them back to the house and have the medics look after them. We'll get them shipped back to the States just as soon as all this is through.'

Kirby's face betrayed the deep anger he felt. These were his men, personally selected by him, the best that money could buy, and they were getting chewed up by a single crazy limey. He looked at Gunn. 'You know something, Leo: this guy is really starting to piss me off.'

Galbraith pulled the door to the rented flat closed behind him, but didn't bother to lock it. There hadn't been a burglary in the town in fifteen years, and that had been committed by passing travellers. He looked up at the top window of the house opposite, where the net curtain fluttered slightly and smiled. Mrs Mulholland, the sixty-year-old spinster who lived there, was a greater deterrent to thieves than any guard dog. She kept watch on the town of Bannock. He waved towards the netting and was rewarded by another flutter. Suppressing a laugh, he moved off towards Main Street.

The pavement was narrow, hardly wide enough for two people to pass each other, and the street was cobbled, like all the others on the western side of the town. At Main Street he turned right and began the long climb towards the police station. Bannock was built on the side of a hill that fell steeply to the River Kyle. Main Street, as the A534 became, neatly divided what locals called the 'Old Town' and the 'New Town'. Galbraith stopped when he was a little more than halfway up the hill, wheezing. Too many cigarettes, too much alcohol and a generally ruinous diet had destroyed his fitness over the years. As he recovered his breath he looked down towards the Marquis of Montrose. The pub had been the first building constructed in the town, sometime in the late sixteenth century, as a house for the water bailiff. The Kyle was elsewhere deep and fast, but on that stretch there was a ford. When the first bridge was built the house became a coaching inn and the Old Town sprawled away up the side of the hill, in a maze of small streets and alleys.

The New Town, a grand name for five rows of back-to-back houses, was constructed in the late nineteenth century, by order of the last of the McLeods. The ever-expanding railway system had fuelled a need for timber and McLeod had built a sawmill, imported labourers from Glasgow and built the cramped little houses to accommodate them. The Laird of McLeod House had also been far-sighted enough to establish vast new timber plantations to replace the trees he cut. The sawmill had been the town's main industry until the 1950s, but now most of the men took the early-morning bus to work in Inverness, thirty miles to the south.

Galbraith's gaze moved across the fast-flowing river to the opposite side of the valley. The trees had a purple tint to their leaves that he'd never seen anywhere else in the world. There was something haunting, almost magical about the place. He took a deep breath and the sharp morning air cut his lungs. 'Come on you, old fool,' he muttered to himself, 'back to the real world, before you start writing poetry.'

'Talking to yourself, Chief Inspector, that's the first sign of madness.'

Galbraith spun round guiltily and immediately broke into a smile.

'Finlay, you scared me out of what little wits I've left. You've been to the station?'

Finlay MacDonald, owner of the Marquis, nodded soberly. 'Aye, somebody stole my bike last night. Enjoying the view?' He nodded towards the river.

'Aye, it's breathtaking.'

The landlord smiled mischievously. 'There's a story that when the Good Lord was making the earth he stopped in a cloud above Scotland with the angel Gabriel. The Good Lord pointed down and said, "This is going to be a great land: it will have majestic mountains, purple glens, running streams of crystal-clear water filled with salmon. It will have golden fields of barley, from which the inhabitants will brew an amber-coloured whisky so delicious others will travel hundreds of miles to drink it. And, for the future, I'll give it oil under its seas, coal under its hills, gas . . ." "Hold on," Gabriel interrupted, "are you not being overly generous to these Scots?" The Good Lord shook his head and replied, "No. Wait until you see their bloody neighbours."'

Galbraith laughed and clapped MacDonald on the arm as he passed him. 'I'll remember that one.'

'You'll no be forgetting my bike, now Chief Inspector?' MacDonald called out after him. Galbraith waved a hand in acknowledgement. As he reached the station a car passed him heading towards the Marquis with two of Braxton's security people in it. Out of habit he noted the registration number. Once in the station, he called for the night reports, sat down behind his desk and lit a cigarette. Angus Mackenzie knocked politely on his door and placed a brown folder in front of him.

'Let's see,' murmured Galbraith, then began to read out loud. 'PC Lang cautioned Dougie Thompson for being drunk and disorderly last night and Finlay MacDonald reported his bike stolen.' He looked up into the sergeant's florid features.

His eyes dropped again to the single sheet of typed paper.

'It's hardly a crime wave, Angus, is it?'

'No, Mr Galbraith.'

'Right, tell PC Lang to pop round to Dougie Thompson's house and have a word with him. That's three times this week. Tell him if there's a fourth he'll be up in front of the magistrates.'

'Right you are, Mr Galbraith.'

'And, Angus . . .'

'Aye, Mr Galbraith.'

'Tell Lang to pick up Finlay MacDonald's bike while he's there.'

Angus smiled. 'Aye, Mr Galbraith.'

The sergeant opened the office door and stepped smartly aside before leaving. Galbraith pushed back his chair and stood up. 'Superintendent Johnstone, this is an unexpected pleasure,' he said.

Derek Johnstone didn't extend his hand. Each man was acutely aware of how he stood in the other's estimation. 'Just what in heaven's name were you playing at over at the Braxton estate yesterday, Chief Inspector?'

Galbraith exhaled a cloud of smoke and relished the look of distaste on his superior's face.

'I paid a visit to Mr Brian Hamilton, to return the passport of Manuel García, an employee of Braxton Industries, against whom a charge of wounding with intent to cause grievous bodily harm had been withdrawn by the Procurator-fiscal's office.'

'And while you were there you took the opportunity to harass Mr Hamilton?'

Galbraith spoke deliberately. 'I told Mr Hamilton that I suspected him of being guilty of perverting the course of justice and informed him I would be making further inquiries.'

Johnstone's face reddened and his mouth contracted into a slit. When he spoke his voice was barely controlled. 'I have seen the file in question and personally spoken to the family of Andy Kerr. The boy made a genuine mistake, for which he is now sorry. There is no evidence whatsoever of any attempt to pervert the course of justice.'

'What about the new car Frank Kerr's driving around in?'

'I talked to Mr Kerr senior about the car. His aunt died and left him some money.'

'The Kerrs are dirt poor. None of the family has had two pennies to rub together in living memory.'

'I am aware, Chief Inspector, of your personal vendetta against Mr Hamilton.'

Galbraith recovered his composure. 'That has nothing to do with it.'

'I think it has everything to do with it. Now, this is a direct order. You will not go near the Braxton estate without my express permission. Is that clear?'

'As crystal, sir.'

'Good, and make no mistake, Chief Inspector: if you disobey this order I will break you so far down the ranks you'll be saluting bus conductors.'

Galbraith blinked hard several times. It was his natural reaction to being threatened. It could have been mistaken for fear, and had been in the past. He'd been threatened, really threatened, only twice before in his life; once by a notorious Glasgow gangster, another time by a corrupt member of the city's council. Both had seen the rapid blinking of the small detective and felt safe. Both were serving long sentences in Barlinnie Prison.

Before Galbraith could answer his superior officer, Angus knocked and entered. He thrust a piece of paper in front of the Chief Inspector. Surprise registered on Galbraith's face as he read it. He looked up. 'I'm afraid something important has come up, sir. Could we continue this later?'

Johnstone stood up. 'I have to visit the other stations. I'll be back in about three hours. If I were you, Chief Inspector, I might use that time to write a letter of apology to Mr Hamilton.' Without waiting for an answer he left.

Galbraith hawked and spat into the waste-paper bin. 'Some chance, pal,' he said softly.

5

Fraser had headed west for over a mile, knowing full well that others would come to help evacuate the two men he'd wounded in the skirmish. The trees were thinner here, so he broke into a trot, holding the AK47 in his right hand. He came to a small hill and leaned into it, hardly slackening his speed. At the summit he paused to take his bearings and turned north once again.

It was close to midday when he slumped down with his back against a tree. He fumbled in his top pocket for the second chocolate bar, then remembered that he'd already eaten it. Almost as soon as he had stopped, the pain in his head had worsened. Suddenly his eyes blurred and dizziness threatened to overwhelm him. He stood and walked in a small circle, breathing deeply and fighting for control. Eventually his vision cleared and the giddiness subsided. It was then that he saw the men.

There were four of them, at a right angle to him, in an extended line. They were patrolling slowly through the wood, rifles at the ready. The nearest was less than ten yards from him. He could see every detail: two AK47s and two G3s; then their faces: all were under thirty. All wore US Army camouflage uniforms and had green sweat bands tied around their heads.

In seconds they must see him. His impulse was to grab for his rifle, some three feet away from him.

'Things are seen for a variety of reasons,' a voice from the past lectured him. 'The shape of the object, its reflection or even its silhouette may be enough to give it away, but movement is by far the surest betrayer of a man's position. Movement, even slow movement, attracts the eye. In close proximity to an enemy, complete stillness will often result in your remaining undetected, even if you are in full view.'

He froze and watched the four men intently. Then he turned his eyes away from the nearest man, observing him with peripheral vision instead. They must see him.

One of the men looked towards him then away again. Sweat trickled down his face. One drop slowly ran down his nose, itching intensely.

His pursuers seemed to move with infinite slowness. He was aware of the silence of the wood, of his own heartbeat pounding in his ears, surely loud enough for the nearest man to hear. They drew level with him and the tree he'd been leaning against gave him some cover. He was about to relax fractionally when the furthest man held up his hand. Simultaneously all four stopped and knelt. Fraser's heart lurched. The desire to grab for his rifle was almost irresistible, but he remained dead still.

The end man produced a map, studied it briefly, then checked the compass hanging round his neck. He pointed north-west and then stood up. The others followed and in seconds they had disappeared from view. Fraser stood frozen for more than a minute before collapsing against the tree. Sitting once more, he pulled his rifle into his arms and cradled it like a baby. The spinning sensation returned and he closed his eyes, but it only became more severe. This time, when he tried to rise he found his legs unable to hold him. When he opened his eyes, the trees swam before him.

He saw himself in a nightmare landscape of twisted rocks and sand under a blazing sun. A man was beside him speaking into a field radio. In the distance, the smoky trail of a rocket streaking into the air.

'That's a confirmed launch, at grid ref 849763. Over.'

'Roger Bravo Thirty, get the hell out of there, they must have spotted you by now.'

'Roger that. Out.'

The man turned to him, with his grinning, handsome face under a mop of unruly red hair. 'As one shepherd said to the other, let's get the flock out of here.'

He followed him, running easily despite the blazing heat, but they had gone only a few yards when the first bullets straddled them. On a low hill to their left a long line of green-uniformed men were firing and sprinting towards them.

He heard his own voice shouting, 'Enemy left. Run, Bob.' Then his rifle was crashing. Two of the green-clad figures went down. He turned, and running with all the speed he could muster, he passed Bob and knelt to give him covering fire. He heard a scream. Bob was down, crimson blood spreading across his camouflaged chest. He ran back and stood above his fallen friend, firing and yelling obscenities. Then he felt a stunning pain in his left shoulder and went down.

The pictures became hazy: a confused mass of dark faces, kicking feet, AK47s jabbing downwards. A shiny pistol wavered before him. He heard words spoken in guttural English: 'You will tell me what I want to know in three seconds or I will shoot you. One, two . . .' Then that face too dissolved and there was Lindsey, leaning over him, telling him he would soon be well, everything would be all right. He tried to touch her and she *disappeared momentarily, only to reappear, screaming for help, running through the woods calling for help, calling for him: 'Mark . . . Mark'.*

He came slowly back to consciousness like a swimmer trying to break the surface. He looked around him in alarm. How long had he been out? He checked his watch: half past twelve. Nearly twenty minutes. He shook his head, afraid the pain and dizziness would return. They didn't. 'Concussion' – the word sprang into his mind. 'Symptoms include dizziness, nausea and, in extreme cases, periods of unconsciousness,' he said to himself.

Instinctively he touched the livid scar caused by the American's bullet which had nearly ended his life. The wound felt inflamed; even the slightest touch sent ripples of pain across his scalp. He would have to deal with it before it became any worse and aggravated the concussion.

A search through his belt pouches revealed no medication that would reduce the inflammation. The forest would have to provide for his needs. Knowing exactly what he was looking for, he began a search of the forest floor. It took him twenty minutes to spot a white and yellow fungus, almost as big as a football, growing along the side of a small bank. *Lycoperdum giantea*, the giant puffball, measuring nearly a foot across: the best styptic nature could provide.

Sitting with his back against a tree, he sliced the fungus into strips and pulped them with water to form a mash, which he spread liberally over his handkerchief and applied to his temple. Almost immediately he felt the powerfully soothing effect. For ten minutes he applied the poultice, occasionally adding cold water to prevent it from congealing. While he did so he considered his latest dreams.

They had disturbed him even more than being hunted. A

thought struck him, and he ripped open his shirt. Clearly visible on his left shoulder was a dull-red, crescent-shaped scar. That part of the dream at least had been real. He rebuttoned his shirt and applied the poultice for another fifteen minutes or so. Then he made an ointment from what was left of the fungus and smeared it liberally on to the wound, which now felt cooler to his touch. Satisfied that his treatment would inhibit, if not stop, further infection, he got to his feet unsteadily.

Immediately his stomach lurched, forcing him to lean against a tree until he felt better. The concussion was starting to kick in. He had to get out of this damn wood, away from these men who were trying to kill him, and seek help. He found his bearings and set off again towards the north.

Galbraith felt like a teenager on his first date. He read the note for the umpteenth time.

> Dear Ian,
> I'll be in town at twelve thirty. Could you meet me for a quick drink in the Marquis?
> Love, Anne

The letter had been totally unexpected. For a brief moment he allowed himself to remember their time together, feelings he'd buried in the dark recesses of his memory; that was until Hamilton had put in that barbed comment at McLeod House the other day. Despite himself a smile came to his face: they had been good times. But that was before Anne had met Hamilton, with his calculated charm and engaging smile. Hamilton had swept her off her feet. They were engaged and married in less than a month. It had nearly ripped his heart out to see her walk down the aisle on another man's arm.

The Marquis was a favourite watering-hole for off-duty Braxton security staff. The two Braxton men he'd seen earlier were seated in a corner deep in conversation, a black briefcase on the table in front of them. He didn't know either by name but dipped his head in response to their greeting as they got up and made their way past his table into the main bar. Then his heart missed a beat as Anne walked through the door still looking as lovely as when he'd first seen her. He stumbled awkwardly to his feet, not sure whether to offer his hand or kiss her. She smiled that glorious smile, grabbed his shoulders and planted a kiss on both his cheeks.

'You look well, Ian. Country life must suit you.'

'I get by. I've got you a tonic.'

'Thanks.' She studied him over the rim of the glass as she sipped.

'I haven't much time. Brian will be here shortly.'

His face must have betrayed his feelings. She reached across the table to grasp his hand. 'I know I've hurt you, but he's been good to me.'

Galbraith glanced away, unable to look into her hazel eyes, unwilling for her to see the pain in his. When he looked back he was once again under control. 'Did he ask you to speak to me?' A look of disgust crossed his face. 'What kind of trouble is he in? If you're here to ask me to drop my investigation . . .'

'It's nothing to do with that,' she told him. Her hand gripped his so hard it hurt.

The urgency in her voice moved him. 'What's he said to you to make you feel like this?'

'It's not so much what he's said, it's what he hasn't said. A woman can tell when things are wrong and things are badly wrong up at that house. There's something else. I'm convinced our calls are being tapped.'

Galbraith forced a smile. 'Now you're being paranoid.'

'Just because you're paranoid doesn't mean they're not out to get you. Isn't that what you always used to say?'

Galbraith smiled again, this time sincerely. 'Trust you to remember that.'

'But honestly, it's not paranoia. There are strange clicks and noises after Brian puts down the phone and once I even heard voices. I haven't been a copper's daughter and a copper's wife without learning a thing or two.'

Galbraith lit a cigarette and inhaled deeply. 'Even if you're right, that doesn't mean he's in any more trouble than he usually is. But in any case what do you want me to do?'

'I'm going to ask him to talk to you.'

'If he's been involved in any criminal activity I won't be able to cut him a deal.'

'Same old Ian. The law is the law. I'd rather see him in prison than hurt.'

'You think it's that serious?'

She nodded.

Galbraith finished his whisky, stood, then leaned forward and lowered his voice. 'Tell him I'm willing to listen and I'll do the best I can for him.' Not trusting himself to say more, he turned and walked swiftly towards the door. In the lobby he bumped into Hamilton. Surprise registered on the former policeman's face as Galbraith jerked his head towards the pub restaurant. 'She's in there.'

As Hamilton squeezed past him Galbraith caught hold of his arm. 'She's far too good for you, we both know that.' They locked eyes, then Galbraith shouldered him aside and stepped into Main Street.

Anne crossed the bar quickly and threw her arms round

Hamilton. He cradled her face in his hands and kissed her.

'I've missed you so,' she said.

'Me too.' He smiled back, then looked over her shoulder to see Galbraith making his way up the street.

'What was he doing here?'

Anne glanced over her shoulder. 'I asked him to come. You know I've been so worried . . . I thought he might perhaps . . . help.'

Hamilton listened, deep in thought. His reply surprised her. 'I'm glad you did. I was going to ask you to visit him anyway. Now listen,' he whispered.

Jackson picked Hamilton up outside the Marquis two hours later. The gangling American was morose and taciturn on their return journey. Hamilton gave up trying to start a conversation and studied the passing scenery.

As soon as Jackson had pulled the Range Rover up outside the main door of McLeod House, he turned towards his passenger and told him, 'Mr Kirby wants to see you straight away.'

Hamilton felt his stomach turn over as he walked up the steps, Jackson close behind. Before reaching the entrance he stopped and turned back. Jackson stopped as well and returned his stare blankly. Hamilton shrugged, trying to appear casual. He felt panic about to overwhelm him. He pushed open the massive oak front door to find Kirby waiting for him in the hall. Gunn, impassive as ever, stood beside him.

Kirby's face broke into a smile.

'Brian, how was your wife? Everything OK?'

'She was fine.' Hamilton grinned uneasily. 'This is a warm welcome.'

'Come inside.' Kirby jerked his head towards the main reception room.

Hamilton followed the smaller man. He was acutely aware of the two others trailing him and could feel the intensity of their stares. Kirby walked to a nearby table on which stood a black Samsonite briefcase. Kirby opened it so that Hamilton could look inside, and when he did so he felt his knees go weak. Gunn caught hold of his arm, his fingers digging deeply into his biceps. He winced with pain. The case held a sophisticated-looking device with a mass of intricate wiring.

'I thought you might recognize this,' Kirby said casually. 'It's the very latest in electronic directional microphones. This little baby can home in on a single conversation at almost a thousand metres and exclude all background noise. Listening to your conversation in a half-empty restaurant was child's play. Listen.' He flicked a switch and Hamilton heard his own voice crystal-clear.

'So that's about the size of it, honey,' he was saying. 'This operation is set to happen soon. It makes everything I've been involved in up until now very small-time stuff. That's why I want you to write to Galbraith – we can't risk the phone. Tell him what I've told you and that I'll cooperate.'

'But Brian,' Anne pleaded, 'why don't you just leave now?'

'I can't. They're already watching me. You must go back to Glasgow today and clear out the accounts in case we have to leave the country in a hurry.'

'I won't bore you with the rest,' Kirby said as he switched off the tape.

'My wife knows everything,' Hamilton stammered. 'If anything happens to me, she'll go straight to Galbraith. You don't know him. He won't rest until he puts you all inside.'

Kirby's face was full of contempt. 'You really don't know

the league you're in, do you, Hamilton?' He turned towards the room's other door. Anne entered, flanked by two security men. When she saw Hamilton she gave a small cry, ran towards him and buried her face in his chest.

'They told me you'd been hurt in an accident.'

Hamilton looked over her head, his eyes locked with Kirby's. Fear was replaced with determination. 'I don't care what you do to me, but let her go.'

Kirby's eyes were emotionless. He walked to a nearby cabinet, then returned with two bottles. 'The Scots make the best whisky in the world, they say. Why don't we all have a drink?'

Fraser was having difficulty focusing his eyes, and the bouts of dizziness were becoming more frequent, the pain in his head more incessant. He stopped to rest his back against a tree. Slowly his legs buckled and he slid down the trunk until he sat at its base, eyes closed, head thrown back, mouth open, gasping in air. Through half-closed eyes the world swam dangerously before him. From far away she came to him again, her beautiful face full of concern.

'I heard you were here, in my hospital. Does it hurt much?'

Her white coat was immaculate, a stethoscope hung around her neck.

'Only when I try to tap-dance.'

His voice was weak. He saw tubes attached to his arms; another ran up his nose.

Her face creased into a worried smile.

'I didn't know you tap-danced.'

'I don't, but don't tell the nurses, it drives them crazy when I try.'

Her smile broadened, then a look of anger swept her face.

'Why didn't you write?'

'I wanted to, but at the time I couldn't tell you what I was doing. Somehow it just seemed better to leave things the way they were until I came back.'

She touched his face tenderly. Her hand was cool and soft; he turned his head to kiss it.

'You fool, you nearly didn't come back, and I would never have known.'

'You were the first person I thought about when I came out of the operating theatre. I asked one of the nurses to contact you, just to see if . . .'

She placed a finger on his lips before bending to kiss him lightly on the forehead. Around him he could hear the shouts of approval from other patients.

'Don't talk now, there will be plenty of time later. I'll be here, I'll never leave you again.'

His vision slowly cleared. He rose unsteadily to his feet and forced himself to start moving, managing twenty paces before his legs buckled once more. This time his jaws locked in an uncontrollable retch that emptied the contents of his stomach in one violent heave. Then, gradually, the dizziness passed. He spat, and pulled himself to his feet. His legs felt much stronger and his vision remained clear.

Holding his water bottle just above his face, he allowed the water to run over it, then rinsed the bile from his mouth. His headache was still raging, but the dizziness and nausea now seemed to be coming in waves. He had better keep moving while he still could.

There were about two hours of daylight left when Fraser came to the edge of the wood. He'd been constantly alert for any sign of patrols, but hadn't encountered one. Dropping on to his stomach, he crawled the last ten yards, pausing in good cover to recce the ground.

Ahead of him lay an expanse of undulating grassland which rose gradually towards the Melville Hills. He calculated the distance to the nearest substantial cover: at least a hundred yards, perhaps a hundred and fifty. As he watched he saw a flash of light. The glint of a discarded tin or bottle? No. There it was again and behind it the slightest movement. Somebody was scanning the tree line with binoculars.

Fraser studied the broken ridge with care for the next twenty minutes. He spotted more movement. There was a line of men in front of him. Slowly and with infinite patience, he began to inch his way backwards. It was over half an hour before he was well into cover and could stand up.

He weighed his next move. The men in front of him intended to stop him reaching the hills. It was reasonable to suppose that once there he would be beyond their control. But if they could keep him bottled up in the woods, sooner or later one of their patrols would find him. His pursuers were inviting him to try to cross the open ground, but could he do it without their detecting him?

In his imperfect memory an idea took shape. He had plenty of daylight left, more than enough time to make his preparations. A short distance away there was an open glade where the grass was similar to the type he had to cross. He walked there and stripped off his jacket, shivering slightly in the late-evening air. Taking some fishing line from his survival kit, he set to work.

First he made four incisions in the back of the jacket, forming a rectangle. Then he threaded the fishing line through the slits to form an oblong loop. Next he chose a clump of grass and fitted it in the loop, making sure that when the jacket was flat the grass would stand vertically rather than lean sideways. When it was in exactly the right position, he turned the jacket over and tied off the fishing line to secure it. He worked steadily, rubbing dark mud on to the surrounding material.

The concentration needed for the task relaxed him, making the pain in his head subside. He began to picture another time he'd prepared to cross open ground just like this.

He saw himself in dark, windswept, barren hills, feeling bitterly cold as the driving rain ran down his neck. His jacket was camouflaged with thick clumps of grass and dark mud and his face was covered with thin netting. Only his eyes were uncovered. He was inching towards a group of very young men.

They all wore helmets and carried Belgian FN rifles; the round, blunt flash protectors at the end of their barrels were silhouetted against the angry sky. He could see their swarthy faces under the dark shadows thrown by their helmets and could hear their mutterings, the angry grumbling of inexperienced conscripts. Their singsong Spanish carried clearly. He was so close he could make out the writing on the side of a missile pointing menacingly towards the night sky. The writing was Chinese and somehow he knew it meant 'Silk Worm'.

As he began to crawl away from their position, pulling a short-barrelled Heckler & Koch 53 assault rifle with him, a patrol was approaching. Two lines of men walked in file, each with a short, thin bayonet fixed to his rifle that caught the dim light and flickered and danced like rows of lighted candles.

He froze. He could clearly make out the face of the patrol commander, a short, fat corporal. There was a shout from the missile site and the corporal yelled in reply. The double line of men switched direction, trundled past him and stepped over a low wall of plastic sandbags to enter the building. He heard the patrol exchanging pleasantries with the men already inside and recognized the soldiers' universal demand for a hot drink.

He began to move again with agonizing slowness as his life depended on him doing just that. Hours later, he stood up and loped into the still dark night towards the distant shoreline, where, on a rocky beach, he met three other men dressed exactly like him. One produced a hooded torch and flashed it seawards and seconds later he could hear the muffled sound of a small boat's engine approaching.

When he came out of his reverie the shadows were already lengthening. His fingers resumed their work, for he was anxious to finish before dark.

6

Galbraith poured himself a large whisky and returned the near-empty bottle to his desk drawer. This he slammed closed, allowing the action to release some of his venom. He swallowed, hoping the scotch would burn out the pain in the centre of his stomach. He hadn't felt that pain for over three years – not since Anne had told him she was leaving him.

She had met him for lunch, just as she always did. As soon as he saw her he knew something was wrong. She forced a smile, then turned her head away when he tried to kiss her, avoiding his eyes. He tried to ignore it, tried to make conversation, but it was like trying to pull teeth, until in exasperation he asked, 'What's wrong?'

It took her a long time to reply.

'This is . . . we're, oh . . .'

Dipping her head, she fished in her handbag for a handkerchief, before bursting into tears. He reached out to touch her hand but she pulled it away. Her head came up, a look of resolution on her face and for the first time she looked him directly in the eye.

'Ian, I don't want to hurt you – but it's over.'

The shock of the words hit him like a physical blow, as the implication of what she had said began to dawn on him.

'Over? What do you mean, over?'

'I can't see you again, not in the way I have.' She reached across the table to clutch his hand, 'but I still want us to be friends.'

He looked at her hand incredulously, as if it was an alien thing. This couldn't be happening, not with his Anne.

'I don't understand. What've I done wrong?'

'It's nothing you've done, it's. . . .'

Like a blind man suddenly given the gift of sight he knew.

'There's someone else,' he said.

'That's not the reason . . .'

He interrupted her harshly. 'Who is it?'

'It's not his fault, it's about us . . .'

'Who is it?' he insisted, his voice almost a shout. People at nearby tables looked at them, alarm on their faces. He twisted his hand from her grasp and clutched her wrist.

She winced with pain. 'Ian, you're hurting me.'

She tried to pull her hand from his but he only tightened his grip.

'I want to know his name – tell me,' he shouted as conversation stopped all around them. Anne looked about her wildly, then suddenly, almost defiantly, spat, 'All right, it's Brian.'

He let her go, rose almost immediately and, ignoring her calls, pushed aside the approaching waiters and stomped out of the restaurant. Hamilton: the name had seared through his brain. Anybody but him. He found him in the station recreation room, playing snooker. The bastard, who had just potted a frame-winning black, glanced up and smiled.

'Ian. Fancy a game?'

As the bigger man stretched to his full height Galbraith grasped him by his tie and shirt front and headbutted him, feeling a savage satisfaction as his forehead connected. Hamilton dropped to the floor. Rolling on to an elbow, he touched the blood pouring from his nose, briefly studied it, then, with the same infuriating smile still on his face, said, 'She told you then?'

'Get up.'

'Don't think I will, thanks – I'm comfortable right here.'

'Get up, you bastard.' Rage consumed Galbraith, who would have kicked the prostrate man if two uniformed constables had not restrained him.

Hamilton sat up, dabbing at his nose with a spotlessly white handkerchief. 'Did she tell you why?'

In response, Galbraith shouted obscenities as he struggled against the men who were holding him.

Hamilton ignored the insults and nonchalantly got to his feet. 'Anne needs someone to love her totally, but you're too much in love with the job to give that kind of commitment. That's why she left you. If it hadn't been me it would have been somebody else.' He walked from the room, oblivious to the other man's repeated taunts.

The next day Galbraith was pulled up in front of the superintendent. No formal charges were laid but he was verbally cautioned for striking a junior officer and posted to another station.

Now, Galbraith smiled ruefully at the faint reflection of himself in his glass. It had taken a year, a year of biting at himself like some animal with its paw caught in a trap, but in the end it had been the job that had saved him. He had lost himself in work. Drink hadn't helped then and it couldn't now. His phone rang.

'Yes.'

'Mr Galbraith.' It was Angus at the front desk. 'Mr Johnstone has just pulled into the car park.'

'Thanks, Angus. Show him right in.'

He finished his whisky in a single gulp and put the glass in the drawer next to the bottle, then walked to the window and lit a cigarette. He hated having to stand when his superior entered a room.

Johnstone entered without knocking, a look of disgust flashing over his face as he smelt the smoke. Galbraith suppressed a smile and motioned for him to sit down. The Superintendent's face was flushed with anger.

'I've just passed the Marquis, where I saw PC Lang, in full uniform, drinking with the owner.'

Galbraith looked suitably solemn. 'I'll have a word with him about it later.'

Johnstone sensed a lack of conviction. 'You'll speak to him now, Chief Inspector.'

'Very well, sir.' He rang the front desk. 'Send in PC Lang, Sergeant.'

'I'll want to speak with you about that earlier matter as soon as you've finished,' Johnstone said, then rose and walked out of the office without another word.

Galbraith steepled his hands and rested his chin on them, gazing into space, until a knock on the door roused him.

PC Lang walked in, a sheepish look on his face.

Galbraith rubbed a hand over his brow, then spoke briskly. 'PC Lang, the Superintendent has informed me that he saw you, in uniform and while on duty, drinking in the Marquis.'

Lang's face went white and his mouth flopped open as if he was about to speak. Galbraith put a cautionary finger to his lips. 'PC Lang, have I ever told you about the bird that flew north for the winter instead of flying south?'

The constable shook his head numbly.

'Well, this bird mistakenly flew north one winter and into

a snow storm. Its wings froze and it fell out of the sky on to an iceberg. A polar bear found the unfortunate bird and, seeing that it was about to die, shat on it. The heat unfroze the little bird's wings and it was so happy it began to sing. A passing fox heard the bird's song, dug it out of this shit and ate it.'

Galbraith smiled up into Lang's uncomprehending face.

'There are three logical conclusions to be drawn from this story. One, anybody who shits on you is not necessarily an enemy. Two, anybody who gets you out of the shit is not necessarily your friend. And three, when you are in the shit, keep your mouth shut. Got that?'

Lang nodded.

'So, anything to say about Superintendent Johnstone's accusation that you were drinking on duty?'

'Nothing to say, sir.'

'Good. Now, I know that Finlay MacDonald is a local councillor, head of the part-time fire service and a special constable. I also appreciate that when you returned his bike he wanted to speak to you about matters concerning the police that he wanted to bring to the attention of the council at their next meeting. Am I correct?'

'Yes, sir.'

Galbraith nodded approvingly. 'In these circumstances drinking with a local official is no more than good public relations.'

A smile of relief spread across the young man's face. 'Thank you, sir.'

Galbraith glared at him. 'Next time Finlay buys you a pint, have the sense to drink it in that back bar where you can't be seen from the street. Now go and tell the Superintendent I can see him now.'

Lang hurried to the door.

'And for God's sake, man, look suitably chastened when you speak to him.'

Lang forced the smile from his face. 'Yes, sir.'

Minutes later Johnstone re-entered the office and, as Galbraith explained about PC Lang's foray into community relations, he had the pleasure of watching his superior's discomfiture.

'Have you considered our earlier conversation about your visit to McLeod House?' Johnstone retaliated.

Before Galbraith could answer the door burst open. Angus stood on the threshold, his normally ruddy face blanched.

'What do you mean by this interruption, Sergeant?' Johnstone demanded.

Angus ignored him, his eyes fixed on Galbraith. 'You'd better come quick, Chief Inspector. There's been a terrible accident.'

It's strange how death diminishes a man. Hamilton lay slumped awkwardly in the front seat of the Range Rover, his face a bloody ruin. Galbraith stood with his hands in his pockets watching Johnstone shouting orders. The Superintendent had insisted on taking charge, leaving him with little to do except observe. He could hardly bring himself to look back at the second figure in the wrecked car. Anne's face was unmarked; she looked almost as if she was asleep. Only the impossible angle of her neck betrayed the illusion. How long he stood there he didn't know. When he decided to walk back up to the road, they were starting to rig lights against the approaching darkness.

The path of the car was easy to follow. It had gouged a deep furrow through a newly ploughed field, coming to rest against one of the county's innumerable tall dry-stone walls. It had crashed through a similar wall fifty yards away. He walked towards it, his breathing becoming laboured as he plodded up the steep bank. He reached the top and saw the road another thirty yards away, across a steeply climbing patch of barren ground.

Galbraith looked from his vantage-point to the Range Rover and back to the road. He decided that it must have been going at well over sixty miles an hour to have travelled so far. He could see where it had left the road: a double wooden guard fence had been demolished. He made his way to it, negotiating the last few feet on his hands and knees because it was so steep.

The car had left the A534 on a notorious bend known locally as the Devil's Horseshoe. Accident investigators from the scene of crime team were taking samples from the tarmac. The two long lines of burnt rubber were plain to see. One of the men looked up as Galbraith approached.

'Evening, Chief. Judging by the length of the skid, this one must have been doing at least sixty when he hit the bend.'

Galbraith looked at him numbly. He recognized the face but the man's name eluded him. He nodded blankly in reply and walked on. The words swirled in his head. Sixty miles an hour coming into the Devil's Horseshoe? He must have been mad or drunk. Bitterness swelled in his throat. First the bastard had taken her away; now he'd killed her.

An image of Anne's face as he'd seen her only that morning came into his mind. He remembered their first kiss, on the doorstep of her father's house. Standing there like an awkward schoolboy on a first date, he'd been unsure whether or not to make the first move. Her little laugh, then she had put her hand behind his head and drawn him to her. It had been as if the world had stood still. Nothing else had mattered except the wonderful warmth and softness of her lips pressed so tenderly against his.

Tears welled in his eyes, and he fought them back with difficulty, hurriedly turning away as a battered ex-army jeep pulled up at the barrier. Momentarily grief dulled his senses but then the driver's face registered.

'Miss Reynolds, the road will be blocked for some time. You'd better head back into town.'

'Has there been an accident?'

'Yes.'

Galbraith's reply made the young woman stop short. He had managed to convey a world of pain in a single word. Charlotte peered closely at his face. It was partially obscured in the gathering gloom, but torment was written in every line of his craggy features. Instinctively she touched his arm. 'Someone you knew?'

He nodded, not trusting himself to speak. But finally years of training took over. 'Brian Hamilton, an ex-policeman who works on the Braxton estate, and his wife, Anne. You really must go back, Miss Reynolds: the road will be closed for hours.'

'Will you be all right?'

He nodded again. 'Superintendent Johnstone has taken charge. I'm just observing.'

Johnstone started making his way up the slope towards them. Charlotte noticed how Galbraith's eyes were repeatedly drawn to the crashed car.

'OK, Chief Inspector.' She jumped back into her jeep and drove off as Johnstone clambered on to the road.

'I don't think there's much good you staying here, Ian.' It was the first time Johnstone had ever used his first name. 'Why don't you go back to the station?'

'When's the post-mortem?'

'I really don't think you . . .'

'This is still my patch.' His words were spoken through clenched teeth.

'Tomorrow afternoon, in Inverness, but don't you think another officer . . . ?'

'No, I'll attend.' Galbraith turned to leave.

'Who was that?'

'Who?'

'That young girl who's just driven off.'

Galbraith answered numbly, his mind elsewhere. 'She's with the National Rivers Authority. She has some work to do in connection with the Braxton estate.'

Galbraith walked slowly back to his car. Behind him Johnstone watched the jeep disappear from sight.

Opposite Braxton's private office, two rooms of McLeod House had been converted into a fully operational hospital ward containing four beds and enough equipment to allow surgery. Although the Braxton team had no surgeon, two of the former Delta Force personnel were highly trained paramedics.

Kirby visited the wounded men. One was heavily sedated so that his leg could be set. The other, Mike Nester, an ex-Delta Force man who had served with him in Somalia, was sitting up smoking a cigarette.

'Those things will kill you, Mike.'

The ex-paratrooper's face broke into a wide grin. 'Got to die of something, Mr Kirby.' With his sandy hair and fresh complexion, even the pain showing on his face couldn't make him look the thirty-five years he was.

'How is it?'

'Not too bad, Mr Kirby.'

Kirby cursed to himself but kept his expression impassive. These men were too good to be doing the job he was paying them to do. 'You were point man,' he pushed on. 'Did you get a look at our target?'

'Saw him very briefly, Mr Kirby, got one clear shot.' His face reddened. 'Missed him by inches, then he just disappeared. One minute he was there, the next gone. I don't know how anybody coulda got out of that killing area without being hit.'

Before Kirby could comment one of the medics put his head round the door.

'There's a cop here named Johnstone. Wants to see you, Mr Kirby.'

The security chief grimaced. 'Keep your chin up, Mike,' he said. 'And if you need anything, ask.' Then he made his way to the ground floor.

The reception room of McLeod House was a magnificent tribute to its former owners. It had been panelled in English oak by its original builder, and each owner had added something and always in excellent taste. The maharaja had contributed a collection of rare jade figures of the Indian deities. Above the Adam fireplace a life-size portrait of Red Hugh McLeod, a magnificent figure over six feet tall, with flowing red hair and full beard, dominated the room. He was attired in full highland dress with a brace of pistols thrust into his belt and a basket-hilted claymore by his side. His right hand was hooked nonchalantly in his waistband within easy reach of both.

Johnstone never tired of wandering round the room but was always drawn to the portrait of Red Hugh. The more he studied it the more he felt the power and dynamism of the long-dead robber baron.

'Vicious-looking sonofabitch, eh?'

Johnstone turned to find Kirby standing only a yard or so from him. The American's entrance had been almost silent. Johnstone concealed his surprise and looked coolly at him before turning back towards the portrait.

'He's magnificent, a man who knew what he wanted and took it.' Johnstone studied the painting for several seconds longer. 'He's also a very distant relative of mine, on my mother's side.'

'Really?' Kirby kept his voice neutral while observing the other man closely. He strolled across to the drinks cabinet and poured himself a measure of Kentucky bourbon. 'Can I get you a drink, Superintendent?'

'Thank you, no. This is an official visit. Actually I'd like to talk to Mr Braxton in person, if that's possible.'

Kirby smiled. 'Mr Braxton is engaged with some very delicate telephone negotiations at present but I'm sure I can answer any questions you may have.'

Johnstone's face remained impassive. 'Very well. I'm afraid I have some very bad news for you. One of your employees, Brian Hamilton, is dead.'

'Brian dead. How?'

'A road accident. His car left the road at the Devil's Horseshoe.'

Kirby shook his head slowly. 'I can't believe it. He had his wife here to visit this afternoon. They were both in this room having a drink with me.'

'I'm afraid Mrs Hamilton is dead too. How much did Mr Hamilton have to drink?'

'Anne dead too?' Kirby swallowed the bourbon as if he needed it. 'That's awful.'

Johnstone nodded. 'How much had Mr Hamilton had to drink?'

'I really don't know. I had a quick one with them and then left them to it, but they must have been here for a couple of hours.' He paused for a second as if trying to remember, then turned back to the cocktail cabinet and raised an almost empty bottle of Glenfiddich. 'Good God, this was full when I left. They must have drunk nearly a bottle between them.' He shook his head slowly. 'The stupid fool.'

'Could anyone else have drunk it?'

Kirby's expression combined anger and sorrow. 'They were the only ones in here.'

'I'm afraid I'll need a statement from you. Could a constable call tomorrow?'

'Sure, anytime.'

'I'll be on my way then.' Johnstone picked up his flat police forage cap.

'Before you go, Superintendent, there is a matter we wanted to discuss with you.'

'Oh?' Johnstone observed Kirby from beneath hooded eyes.

'Maybe you remember that when Mr Braxton first came to McLeod House you and your Chief Constable came over for dinner.'

'Certainly.'

'Mr Braxton was very impressed by you.'

'Having the confidence of a man of Mr Braxton's standing is most gratifying.'

'And rewarding. That's why he gave you that private consultancy on the security of the house.'

A look of concern passed over Johnstone's face. 'I thought that matter was strictly private, between myself and Mr Braxton.'

'As Mr Braxton's Head of Security I am privy to all his security transactions. He would like to put your employment on a formal basis and invite you to join the family, become part of Braxton Industries International.'

Johnstone let a smile spread across his face. He wanted to see more of the other man's hand. 'That is most complimentary. But I'm very happy in my present employment.'

'Mr Braxton realizes that and is therefore offering you the position as head of security at his Tucson, Arizona, oil refinery, with a starting salary of $80,000 and a five-year contract. We would want you to stay on here for another year and work closely with the incoming head of security, just to get the feel of how Braxton Industries operates.'

'A year-long introduction course with me looking at you and you at me?' Johnstone said.

'Exactly.'

'That's a very generous offer, but I really couldn't accept. As I've said, I'm very happy here.'

Kirby's eyes hardened, but his voice remained conversational. 'What *would* you accept?'

Johnstone looked surprised. 'Well, I really don't know. I haven't given the matter much thought.'

Kirby smiled, knowing that Braxton had made at least two approaches. 'Please try.'

Johnstone reflected for several seconds. 'Well, I couldn't consider a move for less than a hundred thousand per annum.'

'A hundred thousand dollars?'

'Sterling. And a ten-year contract.'

'That's nearly double what we pay our other security bosses.'

Johnstone's eyebrows rose as he leaned a little closer to Kirby. 'If you didn't tell them, I wouldn't.'

Kirby locked eyes with the policeman. 'I'll put it to Mr Braxton.'

'Please do. I'll look forward to hearing from you.'

As Johnstone walked purposefully towards the door, Kirby said, 'There was one other matter, Mr Johnstone. Some of my people thought they saw trespassers in the northern woods a couple of days ago. Have you had any reports of strangers in the area?'

'None. In fact the only newcomer is Miss Reynolds.'

'Miss Reynolds?'

'Yes, she's doing some work for the National Rivers Authority. Pretty young girl. She passed by the scene of the accident this evening, but I haven't had the pleasure of talking to her yet.' Johnstone pulled on his cap and gloves. 'Terrible business, this accident. Two people, cut off in the prime of life. Makes you aware of your own mortality.'

Kirby muttered something unintelligible, his thoughts elsewhere.

Parodying a farewell salute, Johnstone turned and almost collided with Hank Burrows and Ike Phillips on the grey stone steps.

The three Braxton men watched as the Superintendent strode towards his car and the uniformed driver slammed the door after him.

'How did things go in London?' Kirby asked.

Burrows brought up his thumb and right index finger in a tight circle. 'A1, Mr Kirby.'

'Good. I'll debrief you in detail later, but now go grab yourselves some food.'

Kirby's face was tight with concentration. He made his way to the operations room, where he walked over to a computer, entered a password, opened a new file and began to type a message. Then, after checking a number, he encoded the message – 'Please check on female aged 25-30 using the name Reynolds who claims to work for the National Rivers Authority. Currently in the Bannock area. Priority one,' it read – and sent it via the computer.

Moments later in Whitehall, a middle-aged man in a pinstripe suit picked up the communication, decoded it and read it with care. He whistled softly to himself as he lifted a red telephone and pressed a button. The call was answered immediately, and the man said, 'Hello, James. We seem to have an unsanctioned operation in progress in Scotland, perhaps by your department. Could you run a check for me on a female, name of Reynolds, age twenty-five to thirty, using the National Rivers Authority as cover? Good. I'll ring back in ten minutes.' He replaced the receiver, picked up the fax and slid it through the shredder.

7

Fraser had begun his crawl into the open ground at dusk. Twilight was the best time to leave the comforting shadows of the woods, for eyes played tricks in the half-light, blurring shapes, turning trees into human forms and making night image-intensifiers almost useless. He had used his hour well. When he lay still his camouflaged back and legs blended perfectly into the surrounding grass.

He had improvised a hood from his shirt tail and woven grass into that too. Even his rifle had grass tied to the butt, stock and magazine. He had bound his trouser legs and sleeves tightly to his body to prevent the loose material rustling as he moved, and discarded everything loose in his pockets. His face was caked with mud, as were all the metal fastenings on his equipment. He was undertaking the most difficult of all military skills: a sniper's stalk.

He extended his rifle slowly until it was about six inches in front of him, then paused, still as the dead. He brought his right leg up, paused again, raised his entire body about an inch off the ground, supported by his hands and right foot, then propelled himself forward with his left leg. He paused every ten feet and lay still for two minutes, counting the seconds in his mind like a free-fall parachutist: one thousand and one, one thousand and two . . . He breathed deeply: in through his nose and out through his mouth. He used the time to relax the muscles in his body to avoid cramp. Satisfied, he repeated the process, listening intently for any sound of the men he knew were in front of him. In an hour he had moved thirty-five yards. He rested again, one part of his mind counting. By midnight he would be safely in the hills.

'How long do you think Kirby'll keep us out here in these God-forsaken woods?' Bill Morley's voice was little more than a whisper, but it betrayed the irritation the young ex-Marine felt at the prospect of yet another night watching the tree line and waiting for the phantom limey to appear.

'He'll keep us here till we find the SOB. Personally, I don't mind how long it takes just as long as I get a clean shot at the bastard.' Sam Weaver pressed his eye to the I-MAC image-intensifier. The tree line appeared, clear as midday, bathed in brilliant green light. The starlight device had been zeroed to Weaver's G3 assault rifle, and he knew that at a hundred yards he could put five shots into a two-inch circle in less than two seconds.

Morley leaned closer. 'Aw, you're just sore 'cause he shot up your patrol.'

Weaver removed the eyepiece and blinked several times to restore his night vision. He stretched, raising both arms high above his head, then slowly brought them down to shoulder level. His right hand shot out and grabbed Morley by the throat. When their faces were only inches apart, he spoke through clenched teeth. 'Damn right I'm sore. Two of my buddies are lying back at the house with holes in them and all I hear is you grousing. Now button your lip, or you won't be able to eat steak for a week.' He shoved his startled companion away from him.

'Geeze, I'm sorry, Sam. No need to get so riled.'

'Shut up.' Weaver's low whisper was urgent. His hand cut off the other man's protests in mid-sentence. He was sure he had heard something.

Fraser heard the Americans arguing. Calculating that they were less than twenty yards from him, he began to circle away and round them. Stretching his rifle forward, he dislodged a discarded drink can, which rolled down a small incline and collided with a stone. The clang it made sounded to him like Big Ben striking. He lay with his face buried in the soft soil and grass, hardly daring to breathe for several seconds, listening to the stillness. He was about to inch away when he heard a faint sound.

The two men were alert now, Weaver methodically scanning the ground in front of him. He saw nothing. Beside him Morley had his AK47 in his shoulder, sweeping it in short tight arcs, searching eagerly for a target. Weaver leaned across until his mouth was almost touching the other man's ear. 'Cover me, Bill. I'm going forward a couple of yards to have a look-see.'

Weaver bounded over the rocks that they were using as cover and dropped to one knee. Lifting his rifle, he surveyed the area through its night-sight. Nothing moved and yet he had heard a sound. He rose and began to walk slowly, in a tight circle in front of his defensive position.

Fraser heard the American approaching. His rifle was under his body; even to try to get it into position would be fatal. He watched as a toecap came into view, only inches from his face.

'Weaver, this is Jackson. Is that you moving over there?'

The radio noise was loud and totally unexpected, prompting a desire in Fraser to grab for his rifle. He resisted it, but only just. He closed his eyes, trying desperately to control his breathing. The urge to swallow was almost irresistible. He willed himself to stay still, forcing his mind to concentrate on his own thunderous heartbeat. Above him the radio crackled again.

'Weaver, is that you in front of your position? Answer, goddammit.'

Weaver stood with his rifle in his shoulder, still concentrating on the open area in front of him. At the second call he let his rifle drop to his side and plucked his radio from its holster at his waist. 'Yeah, it's me. I thought I heard something.'

'You're crazy, man. Moving around like that you're gonna get yourself shot. Get back to your position.'

'Roger that, Jackson.'

Weaver stood for a few more seconds, his rifle hanging in one hand. He continued scanning, trying to decide what it was he had heard.

Fraser studied the boot directly in front of his face. He could see every detail of the stitching, and, above it, the neatly pressed combat trousers. He could hear Weaver breathe, and the metallic click as he replaced the safety-catch on his rifle. His body ached for the relief of violent action.

There was nobody there. Weaver cursed himself for being an overeager fool as he moved swiftly back to his companion. Leaning close, he whispered in Morley's ear, 'Must have been the wind. I guess I'm just getting jumpy.'

To Fraser the words sounded as loud as a shouted

command. He relaxed slightly, suddenly aware he been holding his breath. His chest ached. He let the air slowly out of his lungs. He tried hard to regulate his breathing, his body shuddering as he controlled the instinct to gasp. As sweat streamed down his face, the mixture of dirt and salt stung his eyes, but he fought the impulse to rub them. Slowly his breathing returned to normal.

Weariness swept over him as the adrenalin oozed from his body. The pain in his head worsened, sending flashes of red across his eyes. It was several minutes before he felt able to move again. By now the sweat had cooled on his face, making him shiver slightly. His senses had once again become attuned to the night's sounds. He began to edge forward.

Almost three hours later the grass began to thin. Less than two yards away was a rocky outcrop offering excellent cover. He gathered himself and sprang forward. The joy of standing and simply arching his back once more was indescribable. He stared at the stark outline of the black mountains in front of him as he started towards them, and then stopped dead in his tracks.

The woman's face swam before his eyes again; her name at last came to his lips. Lindsey, Lindsey . . . Her image seemed so close he could touch her. Then it grew even stronger: Lindsey, her auburn hair flying behind her, face contorted with fear, running, branches ripping at her clothes. Lindsey in desperate trouble. He looked back at the woods. She was there, he was sure of it, and in dire need. He leaned back against the cold, hard stone and screwed up his eyes in an effort to concentrate. Lindsey desperately wanted his help. He had to go back.

'I gotta pinch a leg, Sam.' Morley's whisper was urgent.

'OK, crawl back into the rocks, but for Christ's sake be quiet.'

Morley crawled backwards on his hands and knees until he was well into the cover of the surrounding rocks. There, as he stood, he found himself face to face with a figure covered in long grass.

Fraser had barely taken three steps when Morley appeared. The two men swapped stares. They held identical weapons. The American had his in his right hand, clutching it just above its curved magazine. Fraser held his by the pistol grip, its barrel pointed at the ground. He recovered first, bringing his left hand up to his mouth and moving his index finger to his lips, urging Morley to be quiet. The younger man's eyes narrowed, then his face took on a snarl of defiance. 'He's over here,' he screamed, throwing up his rifle to catch it in both hands.

Fraser tilted his own weapon, his thumb knocking off the safety-catch, aimed and fired instinctively. The three-round burst caught Morley in the middle of his chest. The impact punched the man backwards, his rifle spinning from nerveless hands. Fraser bounded back towards the open ground. He had covered barely ten paces when he collided head on with a second man.

Weaver had run towards the gunfire, holding his G3 horizontally across his body. Thrusting the butt of his AK forward, Fraser hit him in the groin and before his opponent's brain could even register the pain, he took a half-step backwards and launched a second blow. This time the compact rifle's butt connected with Weaver's jaw. As the American collapsed Fraser continued to run.

Confusion gripped Kirby's well laid-out line. Men who had been attentively watching the trees ahead were suddenly aware of shots to their rear. In the time it took them to turn, Fraser had stolen twenty yards. He ran in loping strides with his rifle held in one hand and both arms pumping furiously to gain a little more speed. He breathed in and blew out air in short, fast gasps. Every muscle in his body strained for speed. He was three-quarters of the way across the open ground before he was spotted.

From somewhere to his left a single rifle fired three quick tracer shots. The deadly pinpoints of lights arced towards him. In seconds more weapons joined the first, shattering the stillness. The night sky became illuminated with criss-crossing ribbons of light. He could hear nothing above the roar of his own blood in his ears. The tree line was ten yards away . . . nine . . . eight . . . He felt a tug and a searing pain across his left shoulder and almost fell.

A second later he burst through the welcoming trees. Bullets reached into the forest. Ignoring the stinging branches that whipped against his face, he continued to run. Suddenly he found himself in mid-air. He landed heavily, his head thrown backwards on to the forest floor. He hit only soft leaves and earth, but before he could draw air into his tormented lungs he was sliding down a steep slope, eventually coming to rest in a small stream.

He could only lie there, his legs in water up to his thighs, his back resting on the slope. His lungs were on fire and through his closed eyelids flashes of light danced in time to the thudding pain in his head. As his breathing became more controlled he was aware of a new pain. He felt under his shirt and almost sighed with relief. A bullet had seared his shoulder, leaving an ugly burn but not breaking the skin. Above and behind him he heard the low voices of his hunters. He forced himself to stand and began to wade across the stream.

*

Charlotte Reynolds was just finishing a fine meal of game pie and fresh vegetables. She sipped her coffee, checked her watch and looked about her yet again; she was almost the only diner. The highly polished oak tables gleamed and the brilliant hues of the hand-woven carpet gave a sense of luxury and privacy to the immaculately kept room.

On the wall opposite her hung a large oil painting depicting the Marquis of Montrose in battle. Charlotte tried to remember her history lessons. The dashing Scots cavalry leader had joined the Royalists in the English Civil War, she recalled. With an army combining his own personal cavalry and wild highland infantry he had fought thirteen battles and lost only the last. He had been captured after his defeat and beheaded by the vengeful Roundheads.

She looked at her watch again. It was time to call in. She walked into the cool night air. A bank of low, black clouds was rolling in from the west. There would be heavy rain before morning. When she reached the telephone box, a short walk from the Marquis, she checked the contact number for the night and dialled. There was an answer after three rings.

'Hello.'

'It's Charlotte.'

'How are things?'

'Things are very bad.'

'What have you to report?'

'Hamilton has been killed — a car crash. I don't think it was an accident; neither does Galbraith. He's been quite open with me and I think we may be able to trust him after all.'

There was silence for several seconds.

'Charlotte, someone tried to run your name through the

97

company's computer yesterday. I'd had the forethought to remove it before you were deployed but it's a worrying development.'

The only one who had been suspicious of her to her knowledge had been Chief Inspector Galbraith. Had her judgement been so terribly wrong? She pushed the thought from her mind. 'How is your position?' she asked.

'Still secure, but I'm not sure how much longer that will remain the case. You may have to move faster than we both anticipated.'

'Very well, I'm ready.'

'Charlotte . . .' The voice held a note that chilled her. 'There's more bad news. They found Carter this morning, in his flat. He'd been shot. The police believe he'd been dead for a couple of days at least. They're treating it as a bungled burglary. We both know that's not the case.'

Charlotte stared through the grimy glass panes into the darkening sky, her mind suddenly numb.

'In the circumstances I think you should consider aborting the operation,' the voice said.

'Why?'

'I can only offer you limited protection. You were just meant to contact Carter and evaluate his information – not conduct a full-scale inquiry.'

'No. I'll carry on. It's too important.'

'Very well. Be careful, Charlotte.'

She smiled as she heard the genuine concern in the old man's voice. 'I will be.'

She replaced the receiver and walked outside into a night that was colder and darker than before. Turning up her coat collar, she started to walk back to the Marquis. On the far side of the road a man struck a match. She turned to see who it was. The man returned her look and smiled. From the shadows behind him a second figure stepped forward.

'Good evening, Miss Reynolds.' The voice was low and pleasant.

'I'm afraid . . .'

The first man smiled as he drew on his cigar. 'We haven't been introduced. Kirby, Matt Kirby. I'm head of security on the Braxton estate.'

Kirby extended a hand; there was nothing friendly about the small man's grip. Charlotte's eyes flickered to his companion.

'This is Leo Gunn, one of my security specialists,' Kirby said.

Gunn remained immobile.

'How did you know my name?' Charlotte asked.

'A friend of mine in the local police met you at the scene of that tragic accident yesterday. We get so few strangers in this part of the world I thought I had to introduce myself. Especially as you seem to be interested in the Braxton estate.'

Charlotte looked puzzled. 'Interested in the Braxton estate?'

Kirby tilted his head to one side. 'Why, yes. You do want to take samples from the estate's rivers, don't you?'

'In due course, I suppose. I have quite a bit of ground to cover first.'

Kirby laughed and stepped forward to hook his arm under hers and begin to walk her back towards the inn. 'I have a feeling you're a very fast worker,' he said, then paused, before adding, 'You know, my friend told me a lie about you.'

Charlotte swallowed hard. 'Really?' Even to herself her voice sounded thin.

'Sure. He told me you were good-looking. He was wrong. You are quite beautiful.'

'You're very charming,' Charlotte replied, forcing a laugh.

'And you're back at the Marquis safe and sound,' said Kirby. 'And before the rains come.'

'Thank you very much.' Her eyes moved to the other man. 'Your friend Mr Gunn isn't very talkative.'

'No, conversation's not really one of his strong points. Apart from me, Leo doesn't really like white folks; hardly surprising given what we've done to his ancestors over the years. His great grandaddy was the masser's gun bearer. That's how he got his name. It shows how ignorant we white folks were: he isn't even called "gimme the gun".'

The security chief smiled and turned to go, but then, almost as an afterthought, he turned back.

'You know, you really must come and visit us, Miss Reynolds. Here's my card. You only have to ring me and I'll send a car.'

Charlotte accepted the card, her fingers trembling slightly as she took it. 'That's very kind but I have my own transport.'

'I'd rather you didn't drive up to the estate yourself.' He bent towards her, his voice extra low. 'As you've seen already, the roads around here can be very dangerous.' Without waiting for an answer he turned and walked back into the darkness, Gunn following him.

The hunters were making no secret of their pursuit. They crashed through the trees shouting to each other. Torches attached to rifles swung in crazy arcs, lighting up both the trees and sky, conjuring up shadows. Occasionally an overenthusiastic gunman would let off a shot, only to be cursed loudly by his colleagues.

Despite their chaos, Fraser was finding it difficult to keep ahead of them. The darkness made any kind of swift movement through the woods almost impossible. Twice he had almost had his eyes poked out by low branches and his legs were repeatedly being whipped from under him by fallen trees. He stopped to draw in huge gulps of air. Cold sweat made his clothes uncomfortable and his back itched mercilessly from dirt and twigs that had wormed their way under his shirt. If he kept running like this he would either lose an eye or break a leg.

His head ached and another wave of nausea nearly overwhelmed him. Dropping on to his hands and knees, he vomited several times, the taste of bile filling his mouth and throat. When it was over, he rolled on to his back and ignored the sounds of the approaching men. For a while he was oblivious to everything, then, slowly, awareness returned. Hide, he must hide, and let the sweep line pass over him.

He lurched upright and half staggered, half crawled forward until he found what he was looking for: a long-fallen tree some three feet in diameter. He began scrabbling into the soft earth, making a long, shallow trench along its side. His pursuers were close by the time he had finished. He rolled into the trench, covering his body with the dark earth and leaves he had excavated. He drew the Browning; the AK would be useless at such close quarters. Then he covered his head and shoulders with branches and waited. With his ear pressed close to the ground he could detect their advance even more clearly. It wasn't long before the first man clambered on to the fallen trunk.

'How much fucking longer we gonna keep this up, Vince?' he growled. 'We ain't ever gonna find the sonofabitch in this fucking wood.'

The man sat down on the tree above Fraser, his feet kicking the air inches from his face.

'For God's sake, Andy, keep moving,' the second man urged. 'Weaver wants this bastard and he's fit to be tied. You don't wanna be messing with him when he's in this kind of mood.' The two men talked in low whispers.

'Fuck Weaver. He's only mad 'cause this limey has floored him twice.' Andy Ericsson laughed. 'I tell you, Vince, if we keep this up somebody's gonna get hurt.' Ericsson's heel kicked into the tree in exasperation, throwing dirt and bark into Fraser's face. The fugitive closed his eyes.

'Come on, man. If Weaver sees you and reports you to Kirby you'll be in some serious shit.'

Ericsson jumped to his feet. 'Kirby wouldn't have us chasing through these goddamn woods in the dark, I'm telling you . . .'

There was the unmistakable sound of a rifle shot to their left, followed by a scream. Then a voice shouted, 'Get a medic over here. Jackson's been shot.'

'See what I mean?' Ericsson's voice was raised. Others joined in, clamouring for details of Jackson's injuries.

'Everybody hush up.' Fraser recognized Weaver's voice. The others subsided into murmurs.

'OK, listen in, everybody.' It was Weaver again. 'Turn round and make your way back to the open ground and for God's sake make sure your safety-catches are on – Jackson shot himself in the foot.'

Directly above Fraser, Ericsson laughed. 'Serves him right. Big Gulf War vet – can't even take a walk in the woods without shooting himself.' He laughed again. As they started to climb over the log Vince Amato said something in a low whisper that Fraser couldn't catch and both men broke into uncontrolled giggles.

'Vince, Andy, is that you over there?'

'Sure is, Sam.'

'What's so funny? Get your asses over here and carry Jackson back.'

Ericsson swore under his breath before moving off. There were several muted shouts before they found Jackson, followed by a loud scream of pain as somebody trod on him in the dark. Fraser listened as they lifted him, grunting and swearing, their torches swirling crazy patterns of light in the treetops. He heard their voices carry on the still night air as they forced their way through the undergrowth. In time they became only faint echoes and gradually the wood became silent again. He lay there completely still for several minutes.

When he tried to lift his head, he felt suddenly drained of all strength. Pain rippled through him. His stomach knotted again and he turned his head to one side to retch. Only bile came up. He opened his eyes and the trees swam crazily in front of him. He closed them again quickly and felt better, despite the lights flashing against his eyelids.

The pain in his head became worse, a sickening, rhythmic pounding that threatened his sanity. He fought it, forcing himself to breathe slowly. Concentrating on getting as much air into his body as possible with each intake, he used his stomach muscles rather than his chest to power his breathing. Gradually the pain in his skull diminished. When he opened his eyes again the trees remained steady.

The silence soothed him, and even the gunshot burn on his shoulder became tolerable. He felt strangely light-headed and, despite the fact that he was almost covered with earth, like he was floating. He closed his eyes. His ear was pressed against the soft earth and he could hear the insistent beating of his heart. He lifted his head slightly and it stopped. He smiled, then once again laid his ear against the soil, letting the slow, steady sound lull him to sleep.

Kirby stood in the room next to the hospital ward, his eyes fixed on a thick black plastic bag. Gunn stood beside him, as impassive as ever. Weaver forced the bag open as Amato and Ericsson placed Morley's body inside. Weaver was reaching for the zip when the security chief stepped forward and pushed him aside. Kneeling, he ripped open the dead man's shirt to study the bullet wounds in his chest. All three small entry wounds could have been covered by a fifty-pence piece. Kirby pulled a cigar from his pocket and lit it, never taking his eyes off Morley's chest. Without turning his head he spoke to Weaver.

'He only fired the one time?'

'That's right, Mr Kirby: one three-round burst.'

Kirby nodded and motioned to Amato to zip up the bag. He took a deep pull on his cigar and turned to Weaver.

'OK, Sam, give me it again, once more from the top.'

Weaver recounted his story, in short, precise sentences. He blushed openly when he told of his own beating at the hands of their unknown foe. He ended with the sweep through the darkening forest.

'I thought we had a chance of catching him. We could hear him ahead of us but it all went to hell in a bucket when Jackson shot himself.'

Kirby grimaced. 'Not your fault, Sam. You did the best you could. How is the fool?'

'Got a hole in the foot as big as a saucer. He ain't no damn use to us now, that's for sure.'

'And he was definitely camouflaged when you saw him?'

'That's right, Mr Kirby. His face was covered in mud . . . grass all over his back and rifle.'

Kirby shook his head. He began to pace the room and as he stalked back and forth, deep in thought, a trail of smoke followed him. The door was suddenly thrown open by Braxton, who stormed up to him, his face pale with fury.

'Is it true?' he asked, his voice barely under control.

'You mean, have we lost another man? Yes, and another wounded.'

'How in Christ's name is this happening? Your men are supposed to be the best and one lone idiot is making monkeys out of them.'

Kirby became very still and studied his boss through half-closed eyes. Weaver, knowing him well, took a step backwards, not wanting to be too close should he lose his temper. Gunn's head swivelled slowly to observe Braxton. Kirby took a deep breath and let it out slowly; it was the only outward sign of his irritation.

'When you hired me you hired the best. The men that I hire are the best. Does that tell you something?' Kirby's voice was quiet and controlled. He spoke to Braxton as if explaining simple arithmetic to a child. 'This guy has killed three of my men,' he said.

'And Atler,' added Braxton.

'Atler was your man. A low-level thug. I don't count him.' Kirby ignored the look of fury in the tycoon's face. 'Manuel was killed in a knife fight. Manuel was the best damn knife-fighter I ever saw.' He made a throwaway gesture with his cigar hand. 'That could have been luck. But next he ambushes and kills Billy, a full-blooded Apache and a trained soldier. That definitely wasn't. Tonight he managed to cross over a hundred and fifty yards of open ground in front of a line of observation posts manned by ex-combat vets. Are you starting to get a picture?'

'You mean he's trained?'

Kirby pushed his face closer to the bigger man. 'I mean, he's a fucking expert.'

Braxton took an involuntary step backwards. He had never heard Kirby swear before. Kirby let the silence develop between them. He wanted his employer to understand how serious the situation was. When he spoke again his voice was controlled.

'And it gets worse.'

'Worse?' Braxton barely breathed the word.

Kirby's eyes never left his. 'Yeah, worse. Tonight our friend could have got clean away. He'd got behind Weaver's observation post and had a clear run to the hills, but he chose to come back – across open ground, under fire – to get back into the woods.'

'So what does that mean?'

'It means our friend is no longer trying to run away.' Kirby looked from Braxton to his two lieutenants. 'This guy wants a piece of us now.'

8

He was dreaming again and he knew it. A perplexing procession of faces and images passed through his mind. He had seen most of them before: the men outside the house who had tried to kill him; the moustachioed, dark-faced men who had shot him; the Spanish-speaking youths on the barren hillside. There were strangers' faces too, some friendly, some malevolent. Then there was Lindsey, cradled in his arms, her head against his chest, laughing up at him. He was lying in a golden field of corn, the hot sun making him drowsy as he gently stroked her hair.

'Tell me we'll always be together,' Lindsey said, her voice low and earnest.

'We'll always be together,' he said sleepily.

She punched him playfully in the chest. 'Say it like you mean it.'

He opened one eye to study her. 'So you want to play rough, eh?' he said in a poor imitation of a B-movie gangster. Sweeping her round in a tight arc, he tickled her with both hands.

'Bully, tyrant,' she screamed between uncontrollable bursts of laughter.

He stopped frolicking and bent forward to kiss her half-open lips. Their kiss became more urgent. He lifted his head to look into the depths of her eyes and whispered softly, 'We'll always be together.'

'Promise me, Mark?'

Her face began to fade. He tried to hold her tighter in his arms but she had disappeared and he was alone among the ripening corn and blazing poppies.

When he woke, sadness engulfed him, so deep his throat constricted. But in one smooth movement he rolled out from under the log and rose to his feet. His stomach rumbled with hunger. He hadn't eaten a meal for over two days and would need something substantial to maintain his strength. There was plenty of food in this wood; it was just a matter of finding it. Collecting his weapons, he moved off.

Before long he was looking at the side of a hill riddled with rabbit holes. He remained a good distance back and watched his quarry nibbling the short grass. There were two or three main entrances to the warren; the rest were just escape holes. As he began to advance, its inhabitants scampered away. Taking the survival kit from his belt, he undid the three snares it contained, set them, then retreated.

Minutes later the rabbits began to reappear. None had used the main entrances, no doubt because of his scent or the noise he had made outside them. He waited expectantly until there were at least a dozen rabbits of varying sizes in view, then ran towards the burrow waving his arms. The startled creatures once again darted for cover, one of them into an entry hole, where its leg caught in a snare. He picked it up by its back legs and dispatched it with a single chop to the back of the head.

Then he moved a good mile away and dog-legged his way back to see if his foray had been detected. When he was satisfied that it hadn't, he skinned the rabbit, sliced and diced the meat into the steel mug and covered it with water. At the foot of a tree he made a small fire and balanced the mug over it between small stones. When the meat had boiled for about thirty minutes he sat down against the tree and savoured every mouthful. His meal finished, he leaned back, feeling better than he had at any time since being shot at the waterfall.

He considered his next move. He had made the decision to return to the wood without any clear plan of action, but now was the time to think ahead. He studied the map. There were two areas circled in red. In one the legend 'McLeod Manor House' was printed in bold Old English letters. The other marked the point where the contour lines concentrated abruptly. He peered closer to read the small print alongside the second circle. 'Danger. Potholes', it read. He calculated he was closer to these than McLeod House, so they would be his first destination.

He stretched and burped contentedly. Whatever lay ahead he was ready for. He set off at a brisk, mile-eating pace, swapping the AK47 from hand to hand every ten minutes or so to ensure that neither arm became deadened by its weight.

It was an hour later that he came across the tracks. He knelt to study them more closely. A number of men, travelling in single file, had passed that way sometime that morning, moving north to south, cutting directly across his westerly path. The tread patterns were all similar except for a footprint that had a deep groove running across its tread. He was sure they were made by US Army boots.

He picked up a stick and drew across the track two short lines about eighteen inches apart, to represent a stride, then counted the number of footprints within the lines. There were four. He repeated the process twice more and the answer was the same each time. It was probably the patrol that had nearly run into him the previous day. Standing, he looked about him: the wood suddenly appeared more menacing. He moved on more cautiously.

A little later he cut the tracks again, this time moving in a northerly direction. He studied them with care, having recognized the scarred tread. The men were searching for him more methodically than they had until now. He had to put himself in their position if he was to understand their movements. What did they know about him that had made them change their search pattern?

He pulled out the map and their plan of action was immediately apparent. To the east, just over half a mile away, was a wide track; to the west, the boundary fence. So, they knew where he had re-entered the forest last night and had calculated how far he had gone since first light. They were cross-graining: moving across his intended line of march, trying to pick up his tracks using the track and the boundary fence as perimeter guides. No doubt both would be heavily patrolled. Once they found his intended route it would be a simple matter to stay on it and radio ahead for another group to lay an ambush. He would either be hunted down by the patrol or caught by the stopping group. If he hadn't spent time foraging for food he would be smack in the centre of their search pattern.

What to do? Going back was out of the question, while going forward meant having this patrol on his back and possibly being trapped between the two. The answer was to neutralize the patrol, but he lacked the fire-power or ammunition to take on four trained men. Besides, the sound of shots would alert those ahead of him. He thought carefully and a plan gradually took shape.

He started forward again, careful to measure the distance covered by counting every time his left foot touched the ground, a length equivalent to one yard over the country he was crossing. Twenty-five minutes later he cut the tracks again, going south. He estimated that he had travelled fifteen hundred yards.

The tracks were fresh, the edges of the footprints clear and sharp. He went on, counting out his fifteen hundred yards. Thirty minutes later, having found no tracks, he stopped. He marked the spot, then went forward for another ten minutes to make sure there were no signs, backtracked to his original position and turned in the direction from which the patrol would come.

A small but deep and rapid stream cut across his path. A fallen tree formed a passable natural bridge over it and from his end a narrow but clearly defined animal track bent round the steep ground, forming a natural funnel.

Aware he had little time, he took four steps along the faint track and marked the ground with a piece of wood. He tried to picture in his mind what would happen. Then he took a step to the left and marked the ground again.

After stripping off his jacket and spreading it out on the ground, he cleared away the leaves and topsoil and placed them to one side. Next, using his knife, he began to dig the lighter, sandy-brown soil and threw it on to his jacket. Having dug a rectangular hole roughly eighteen inches long by a foot wide and two feet deep, he carried the spoil twenty yards off to the left and dumped it, then carefully covered the light-coloured earth with fallen leaves. He cast around beneath the trees for fallen branches and finally chose four sticks of about an inch in diameter and eighteen inches long and eight of about half that length.

Using his knife like a hatchet, he sharpened both ends of the sticks. The longer ones he hammered into the bottom of the hole, spacing them evenly along its length and then re-sharpened the exposed ends. The others he pushed into the sides, three each on the long sides, two on the top ends. The stakes at the bottom were unlikely to pierce the tough soles of the boots his pursuers were wearing but they would turn a foot awkwardly. At best the trapped man would be stabbed in the lower calf by one of the side sticks; the worst that could happen to him would be a badly sprained or broken ankle.

Swiftly he wove a net of thin branches over the top of his trap, covered it with a layer of leaves, then a layer of dark topsoil from his coat and finally another layer of leaves. He moved to his second marker. He anticipated that when the first man was injured the second would step to his left to get round him and offer assistance. He dug another hole exactly like the first, all the while listening intently for any sound that might warn him of the approaching patrol. When he was finished he went to the stream and, walking backwards, carefully erased any sign of his presence. Stepping over both the traps, he backed down the track for ten yards, brushing and covering his tracks. He took a long look to satisfy himself there was nothing that would distinguish his handiwork from any other patch of woodland. Then he turned and strode quickly towards the west.

The scream, long and high-pitched, was followed by a stream of invective. He stopped to listen. A slight smile played across Fraser's lips.

'Any second now,' he said softly to himself.

There was a second scream in a deeper, harsher tone, then more obscenities and a babble of voices. His smile broadened and he gave a low chuckle. Two things occurred to him: he was pretty good at this, and he was starting to enjoy himself.

*

Galbraith could never get used to the smell, a mixture of antiseptic, preservatives and decaying flesh. His eyes were continually drawn, against his will, to the two sheet-covered bodies lying still on the mortuary slabs. Two attendants moved around the tables, cracking the occasional joke. He felt an overwhelming urge to yell at them, to tell them that one of these still forms was Anne, his Anne. But he didn't, knowing they meant no harm and that their banter helped shield them from the unpleasant nature of their work.

Behind him a door opened. A tall, white-coated man in his late fifties advanced towards him, a sheaf of papers in his hand. He had the long stride of a hill-walker and a mane of white hair. He peered down at Galbraith, his unkempt eyebrows rising to allow his startlingly clear blue eyes an unrestricted view of him. There were laughter lines at the corner of those eyes. Mungo Campbell, registered state pathologist, was a man who enjoyed life despite his work. A faint smile tugged at his lips as he observed the chief inspector. They had met before and the wee man's caustic sense of humour had been much to his taste.

'Well, Mr Galbraith, what have you brought me this time?'

'Double fatality. Road accident,' Galbraith murmured.

The smile left Campbell's face. In those four words he heard an ocean of pain.

'Did you know the deceased, Ian?'

For a second Galbraith's throat constricted. He nodded. Eventually he pulled himself together enough to mutter, in a cracked and hollow voice, 'The man was in Glasgow CID with me, the woman . . . might have been my wife.'

Campbell was no stranger to grief. He placed a huge hand on the policeman's shoulder. 'I'm sorry, laddie, but as you know only too well, there are formalities to be gone through.

We'd better get them done, then you can be on your way to grieve in private.'

Galbraith nodded and followed the big man to the tables. With a practised flick of his wrist Campbell threw back the covering sheet. 'Can you formally identify this man?'

Galbraith read from his notes. 'Yes, I formally identify him as Brian Hamilton, age thirty-six, presently employed as a public relations officer.'

Galbraith watched as the pathologist replaced the sheet and walked slowly round to the other table. He steeled himself. Campbell flicked back the sheet. She looked so peaceful. He fought back the tears.

The other man's voice came from a long way away. 'Ian, can you identify her?'

Galbraith looked up into his face and spoke deliberately, his voice hollow and without emotion. 'Yes, she's Anne . . . Anne Hamilton, wife of the other deceased, age thirty-four, occupation housewife.'

'OK, Ian, wait next door. I'll call you when it's over.'

As Galbraith walked into the adjoining room, it seemed to take all his will-power just to move his legs. He collapsed into a chair and, ignoring the prominent 'No Smoking' signs, lit a cigarette. Sleep had been impossible the night before. His mind had been tortured with images of Anne and of their time together. Deep down he had always hoped that one day she would see Hamilton for what he was. He had always hoped she would come back to him. Anger briefly flared inside him: anger at Hamilton, anger at the world for robbing him of Anne, and when it was gone it left a strange emptiness. He was unaware of time passing.

When the door opened and Campbell appeared, stripping off a pair of rubber gloves, Galbraith looked at his watch and was startled to discover that he had been sitting there for two hours. He rose slowly to his feet, weary beyond measure.

'Well, what did you find?'

The pathologist motioned him to sit, went to a nearby table and poured them both a cup of sweet tea. He handed one to Galbraith and sat opposite him.

'Death,' he began, 'was caused in both cases by trauma to the neck.' He consulted his notes. 'The injuries are consistent with severe whiplash. I believe the accident happened at the Devil's Horseshoe?'

Galbraith nodded.

'Yes, that would produce trauma entirely consistent with their injuries. I ran blood alcohol tests. The driver's blood contained nearly three times the legal limit.' He looked up. 'Is there anything else you need to know? You'll be getting a full written report.'

Galbraith sat in silence, hardly registering the words. He felt old and tired. 'No, I'll get all I need from your report. Thanks, Mungo.' He turned and shambled to the door, where he paused.

'There is just one question I'd like answered, if you can. Did she suffer at all?'

Campbell shook his head, his wild mane of white hair lashing his shoulders. 'No, death would have been almost instantaneous.'

Galbraith forced a smile. 'Thanks, that's something at least.'

The other man returned the smile. 'Besides, she was probably asleep,' he added.

'Why do you say that?'

Campbell smiled apologetically, embarrassment showing in his face. 'She was even more drunk than her husband.' He glanced down at his notes again. 'Her blood alcohol level was 210 millilitres of alcohol in 100 milligrams of blood – one of the highest I've ever seen.'

'What!' The word exploded from Galbraith. 'You're saying Anne was drunk?'

Campbell took an involuntary step backwards. 'Yes,' he said.

'Did you do an internal examination of her stomach?'

'No, it's not normal practice when the cause of death is so . . .'

'Do it.'

Campbell opened his mouth to reply, thought better of it and returned to the examination room.

Galbraith paced the floor, his steps short and urgent. He smoked one cigarette after another until the pathologist appeared again about ten minutes later.

'Don't tell me, I'll tell you,' the policeman said curtly. 'You found ulcers – peptic ulcers – didn't you?'

'Yes. Four of them.'

'Tell me, Mungo, what would have been the medical effect of someone with that condition drinking the amount of alcohol you found in Anne?'

'Unless she got to hospital inside a couple of hours at most, she would have died. As it was, one of the ulcers had already perforated, causing massive internal haemorrhaging.'

'How would she have been feeling?'

'After two or three drinks she would have been in great pain; with this amount, agony. Why would somebody with her condition be foolish enough to drink that much?'

'She wouldn't. Anne's had those ulcers since she was in her early teens. One drink was enough to make her throw up.' He paused. 'But the person who poured it into her wasn't to know that.'

The trees were throwing long shadows on the forest floor when he reached the site of the potholes. He had spent some time covering his tracks. Ahead of him the ground rose sharply. The trees became more stunted nearer the top of the rise and through the topmost branches he could see the sky, which indicated open ground beyond.

He set off, walking from shadow to shadow, tree to tree. Every three or four steps he paused and, turning his head from side to side, he tried to catch any sound that might warn of danger. When he was about thirty yards from the summit he slowed his pace even more and took infinite care to move as noiselessly as possible. At each step he put the outside edge of his foot down first, tested the weight, then slowly rolled the ball down, feeling for any loose rock or dry stick that might move and betray his presence. Only when he was satisfied that his footing was secure did he transfer his full weight on to the foot. All the time he scanned the area around him, starting at his feet, moving up to the ground midway between himself and the rim's edge and finally the rim itself. Even so, he almost missed the sentry.

He heard the rasp of a match and froze. The sound had come from his right and very close by. Cautiously he turned his head. At first he saw nothing, then a trickle of smoke and the faint outline of a man's head just inches above the ground. There was a lookout position dug in at the base of a tree about ten yards from the site.

He dropped on to his stomach and crawled thirty yards to his right before once again heading for the ridge. Just short of the crest he eased himself in among the foliage of a bush.

The ridge formed the edge of a natural amphitheatre about half a mile in diameter. To the west the ground sloped steeply on both sides to form an immense 'V' through the apex of which ran an artificial road, made up of metal plates a foot wide and a yard long, held together by thick corded rope. The road led to a cave entrance almost directly opposite him. A long line of electric lights was strung from the cave mouth and seemed to stretch deep into its bowels. He could hear the hum of a generator. From his position he could see that the cave formed a steep passage leading into a network of tunnels. Several smaller caves dotted the hillside.

As he watched, a man wearing a hooded white boiler suit and carrying what looked like a pneumatic drill emerged from the tunnel's mouth. The man dropped his gear at the cave entrance, removed a pair of goggles, threw back his hood and spat. A second man appeared, identically dressed and carrying a coiled length of red cable. He threw it down next to the drill and began an animated conversation with his partner as both men stripped off their overalls.

From behind him Fraser heard the sound of an approaching vehicle, the muffled squeal of brakes and doors being slammed. He hugged the ground even closer. Glancing to his right, he saw a man silhouetted against the skyline. Moments later another appeared directly opposite him on the far side of the basin. The two men waved to each other and those below, then disappeared. He breathed a little easier and turned his attention to the activity below.

A Range Rover was making its way slowly along the artificial road, up to the cave mouth. The occupant got out and threw a flask to the nearest man. Fraser could hear the workers' shouted thanks. The flask catcher poured two cups of steaming liquid. Fraser's mouth watered slightly; a cup of hot, sweet tea would be very pleasant just now. It was odd how much you missed the little things when you were in the field.

Below him the seated men rose. One pulled out a G3 from the Range Rover and threw it to the man who had been driving. The two others tossed their white overalls into the back of the vehicle, climbed in, spun the car in a tight arc and drove back along the road and out of view. The man with the rifle settled himself down in the cave entrance.

Fraser eased himself back from the edge and rolled on to his back. There were at least three sentries – two on the perimeter and one in the main cave entrance – so trying to gain access there would be futile, but if the smaller caves did link up with the central tunnel's entrance passage, they would be his best bet. He glanced up at the darkening sky. There would be no moon tonight. In about two hours it should be easy enough to slip over the rim and investigate. He decided to get some sleep. Making sure his rifle was within easy reach, he folded his arms and closed his eyes.

'I checked Charlotte Reynolds through all the Home Office computers, Mr Braxton, and came up with a complete blank.'

Braxton and Kirby sat on one of the twin green leather Chesterfields in the main reception room of McLeod House. Gunn stood by the door.

'Matt is still very suspicious of her,' Braxton replied, his tone neutral. He didn't like his guest. He didn't like limeys in general, but he held an especial contempt for Sir Marcus Brown, Permanent Under Secretary of State for Industry. It wasn't that he was corrupt and greedy: it was the arrogance of the man, his unwavering assumption that his ancestry and upbringing made him superior. Not that Braxton let it show, for he needed Sir Marcus, needed him to pull all the strings and oil all the wheels in Whitehall; so he suffered in silence. He would do so until Operation Hades was complete. Then perhaps he'd give it a year or two and send Kirby over to settle the score with this vain little peacock. The thought warmed him. He smiled.

Sir Marcus smiled too, revealing a set of perfect teeth that had cost him a small fortune in Harley Street. 'That's Mr Kirby's job, to be suspicious of everyone, is it not?' The civil servant inclined his head apologetically. 'No offence intended, Mr Kirby.'

The security chief returned the smile. 'None taken,' he replied.

Years spent in boardrooms all over the world had taught Braxton the benefits of concealing his thoughts, yet he studied Sir Marcus with barely suppressed distaste. The man's scrawny body was encased in a hand-tailored silk suit. Strands of hair, parted just above his right ear, were draped over his gleaming pate and an over-large, slightly hooked nose, thin lips twisted into a permanent sneer and a small, pointed chin completed the picture. Jesus, Braxton thought, there's a face only a mother could love and a father would never tire of hitting.

'If you could get me a copy of her fingerprints I could have a more thorough check carried out,' Sir Marcus continued.

Kirby thought for a second before replying. 'I think I can get them to you within twenty-four hours.'

'Splendid.' Sir Marcus flashed his expensive smile and took a sip of tea. 'Now to matters of more immediate concern. Hades is due to begin in days, although I must confess I would have liked more time to prepare.'

'Speed was of the essence. I only just managed to get the

shipment out of my plant before the inspectors came in,' Braxton told him.

'Yes, you were lucky that shipment of spent fuel rods was ready to be shipped to Dunston for reprocessing. How are your current preparations proceeding?'

'Everything's on schedule. The receiving point has been prepared. What about your end?'

'There have been some difficulties and, I'm afraid, some additional expenditure.'

'Additional expenditure?' Braxton repeated softly.

Kirby noted the change in his employer's tone. Behind him, Gunn's huge head swung slowly round as if at a single word of command he would pull the man apart.

Sir Marcus seemed totally unconcerned by the effect of his words. 'Yes, due to unforeseen circumstances the operation is going to cost a little more.'

'What unforeseen circumstances?' Braxton said.

Sir Marcus took another sip of tea. 'Well, the death of Carter for a start.'

Braxton threw a glance at Kirby and was about to reply when Sir Marcus stilled him with an upraised hand.

'Please don't insult me by denying that you killed Carter, and on this very estate. He informed me that he wasn't happy about Hades and that he was coming up here to have it out with you.' Sir Marcus's lips compressed into a smile. 'The poor man trusted me, you see, wanted me to inform the security services, which, of course, I did not.' He gave an exaggerated sigh. 'And the next moment he is found dead at his flat in Bayswater. As his superior I was kept fully informed of the police investigation. According to their reports he was killed the day before his body was found. We both know he was here at that time. No doubt some of Mr Kirby's people deposited him back in London.'

'What is the police view?' Braxton asked.

'They still believe he was killed by an intruder and lay undetected for forty-eight hours.'

Kirby leaned forward. 'Did Carter tell anybody else that he was coming up here?'

'Only me as far as I'm aware. I told him not to discuss it with anyone else until he had talked to you. But this is a minor matter. Of more importance is that one of the containers started to leak and needed reinforcement.'

'How bad was it?' Braxton was suddenly concerned.

'We caught it in time, but I'm afraid Charles Webster now suspects the true nature of the contents.'

Braxton thought for a second before replying. 'What has he said?'

Sir Marcus inclined his head. 'That if he had known before, he would never have agreed to his station being used to store the material. He also said it was an abomination and that something has to be done.'

'Do you think he'll go to the government?' Kirby asked.

'It won't come to that,' Braxton said firmly before Sir Marcus could reply. 'Have the helicopter ready in twenty minutes. I'll pay Charles a visit. Anything else, Sir Marcus?'

'Yes, the method of payment.'

'What do you want?'

'As I'm sure you're aware, the situation in Congo is very volatile at the moment. Certain parties I represent want to give covert support — support that cannot be traced back to them — to the Tutsi rebels in the south. The Tutsi government in Rwanda has agreed to act as a conduit for an arms shipment to the rebels. We'd like you to arrange it.'

'What do they need?'

Sir Marcus consulted a list. 'Five thousand M16 rifles, fifty M60 light machine-guns, 200 LAW anti-tank rockets and two million rounds of 5.56 ammunition – to be delivered to Kigali within three weeks.'

Braxton looked at Kirby and saw his nod of acknowledgement. 'We can do it. Give Matt your contact in Kigali. That's a very expensive extra payment, Sir Marcus.'

'I'd have thought it cheap considering the penalties that would have been enforced if the US Atomic Energy Commission ever found out about the contents of the Hades containers.'

Before Braxton could answer they were interrupted by a knock on the door. Weaver walked in and handed a note to Kirby, who read it without emotion and passed it to Braxton.

'Trouble?' Sir Marcus asked.

'No, just some last-minute details that have to be attended to. I'm afraid I'll have to continue with this later. A room's been prepared for you. I'll see you when I get back.'

Every bed in the makeshift hospital was full and the hapless Jackson was forced to sit in a chair nursing his wounded foot while the newest casualties were treated. One gave a loud grunt of pain as his boot was cut off. Kirby walked over to the table and looked over the medic's shoulder. 'How bad is it?'

The medic carried on with his work as he replied. 'Bad enough. Both these guys were speared through the lower calf. Jones here's got a broken ankle as well.'

Kirby turned and walked over to the patrol's commander, a powerfully built ex-Ranger in his early thirties whose face was like stone as he watched the medic operate on his two men. He dragged his eyes away to address his superior. 'Pungee traps, Mr Kirby, like the Viet Cong used. Two pits. Hank stepped into the first one, dug into a track we were walking along, and Eddy tried to help him and stepped into a second. He picked the ground to perfection: there was no way we could have avoided them.'

Kirby thought for a second. 'Come with me, John.' He walked swiftly to the operations room, followed by the patrol commander, Braxton and his two lieutenants. 'Show me exactly where the traps were,' he said, indicating the large-scale map of the estate pinned on the wall.

The patrol commander concentrated for a second and then pointed. 'Right there, Mr Kirby.'

'He's heading for the potholes. Didn't want the patrol picking up his trail and warning the boys there,' Kirby said, more to himself than anyone else. 'He's smart, real smart, but this time he's been a little too clever for his own good. How many men are up there at the moment?'

'Just the four sentries. The last of the workers left just before last light,' Weaver answered.

Kirby turned swiftly, his face alight with purpose. 'Sam, get on the radio, tell all the boys on the stopping line to make their way to the pick-up point, then organize transport to take them to the potholes. Leo and I'll make our way there and link up with them.'

'What's your plan?' Braxton asked.

'I'm gonna surround those damn holes and search every rock and tunnel.' He looked back to the map, a smile of triumph on his face. 'He's in there, I'll stake my life on it. This time he won't get away. I'm gonna find him and finish this once and for all.'

9

The Sikorsky dropped gently just outside the perimeter fence. Braxton waited until the rotors had stopped spinning before undoing his seat belt. The pilot made his way down the length of the helicopter and opened the gull-wing door to allow him to step down. The tycoon stretched to his full height and looked at the brooding sky. He wanted to get this meeting over quickly and get back to McLeod House. A car sped towards him and pulled up. The uniformed driver got out and tipped his hat. 'The Director was informed you were coming. He is waiting to see you.'

Braxton nodded to the pilot to remain and seconds later was speeding through the gates past a red sign reading: 'Dunston Nuclear Power Station. The Safe Way To Future Energy Requirements'.

Minutes later he was ushered through a door marked 'Station Director'. The empty room was furnished with a huge rosewood partners' desk and an incongruous, early-Victorian statuette of a brightly dressed black boy holding a drinks tray. Braxton wandered around, idly studying the reproduction watercolours. It reminded him of his office back in the States, except that his paintings were genuine masterpieces. A door opened behind him.

Charles Webster was a striking figure. At sixty-three years

of age he stood ramrod straight and well over six feet tall. His broad features looked as if they had been chipped out of stone, his eyes from citrines. They were usually warm and friendly, but in anger they grew suddenly cold and glazed. At the moment they were glacial.

Webster ignored Braxton's outstretched hand, sat down and gestured to him to take the seat opposite. Braxton complied and, with his chin supported in one meaty hand, studied the power station director across the expanse of desk.

Webster spoke first. 'I know, Edward.' His voice, normally deep and steady, quivered with barely controlled anger.

Braxton remained impassive. 'What do you know, Charles?'

'I know about those containers.'

Braxton glanced at his reflection in the dark, undraped windows, then back to Webster. 'I paid you a small fortune to store waste in this facility until I could dispose of it. I see no reason for you to get upset now.'

Webster's face mottled with anger as his self-control ebbed away. 'It's not just toxic waste – it's pl. . .'

'Don't go on,' Braxton interrupted. He leaned down to pick up a slim leather briefcase. 'You're married, aren't you, Charles, with two daughters? Didn't I read somewhere the other day that Tiffany is shortly to marry some American millionaire?'

'My family has nothing to do with this, Braxton.'

Braxton noted a change in Webster's tone: the anger was still there, but it was edged with caution. Braxton now had his briefcase open on his lap. 'Do you remember the Far East convention we attended together three years ago? How to meet the region's future energy requirements? Our hosts provided some wonderful hospitality, didn't they?' His eyes narrowed. 'Funny thing, though: I remember you never came to the brothels or sex shows – you always went to bed early. I don't trust people who go to bed early.' Braxton tossed a handful of photographs on to the desk. Webster closed his eyes. In the harsh electric light the flesh tints formed an elaborate pattern against the red leather desktop.

Braxton picked up one of the photos. 'These boys can't be much older than nine or ten.'

He closed his briefcase, stood and walked to the door.

'I want those containers strengthened, Charles. Operation Hades goes ahead as planned in two weeks. You can keep the photos for old times' sake.'

He had gone before Webster could say a word.

Lindsey was with him again, running just ahead of him, hair gleaming with tiny droplets of rain, head thrown back as she laughed, so close he could almost touch her. The top of the hill was near, and she stopped as she reached the crest, hands on hips, grinning in triumph.

'I've won, I've won, sluggard.'

'You cheated,' he gasped.

Her face took on an expression of mock anger. 'Nonsense, you're just a bad loser.'

'You tripped me.'

'Never. It's not my fault you have such big feet.'

He growled and grabbed at her, but she danced away nimbly, out of reach.

'Concede defeat.'

He caught her arm, pulling her to him, feeling the warmth and softness of her body, the firmness of her breasts. Her eyes danced with mischief, then softened, then closed. He kissed her, feeling the darting energy of her tongue as it forced its way into his mouth. The rain beat against his back; he ignored it. Suddenly her lips broke from his and she buried her head in his chest. He felt her sob. Cupping her chin with his hand, he lifted her head to see tears mingling with the rain on her face.

'What's wrong?'

'Nothing,' she whispered.

'Tell me.'

She buried her face in his chest again, her arms pulling their bodies together.

'I'm afraid.'

'What are you afraid of?'

'Of this. It's so perfect. Something so perfect can't last, it can't.'

'I told you we'll always be together, always. Besides it's not perfect I've got big feet, remember?'

She was out of his arms in a second, twisting round behind him. He reached for her again and fell, when he looked up she was running down the hill, hair streaming behind her again.

'Slowcoach, I'm going to beat you down the hill as well.'

He was getting to his feet as she started to fade. Softly he called out to her: 'Lindsey.'

Fraser sat bolt upright, listening to the night sounds, his senses tuning in to his surroundings. Everything was still, almost peaceful, but something was missing: there was no dull ringing in his ears and the headache that had become so much a part of him had disappeared. He felt ten times better than when he had fallen asleep.

He rolled on to his stomach and crawled up to the edge of the amphitheatre. Apart from the well-lit entrance to the main cave, he could see little in the darkness. It was as good a night for skulduggery as any thief could want. He stifled a low chuckle and bellied over the rim. Using his elbows and knees to propel him, he glided almost noiselessly downwards, his stomach barely brushing the grass. He paused every ten feet or so to listen, then continued worming his way forwards. Three-quarters of the way down he changed direction, turning sharply to the left, to go around behind the main cave entrance and the sentry.

The ground was more uneven and scattered, with loose rocks which slowed his progress. As he neared an entrance to one of the smaller caves he became more aware of the generator. Its rhythmic throb seemed to vibrate the very ground over which he crawled. He rested again, listening to its relentless thump and feeling the cool night air drying the sweat on his back. He was less than ten feet from the entry to the small cave. As he moved forward again his right toecap dislodged a rock the size of a football. He watched in horror as it tumbled down the hill, gathering speed, to smash into a larger rock just beside the main cave entrance with a noise like a pistol shot.

He shifted the AK into a firing position and sighted it on the entrance. There was nowhere to run to or hide. He could only wait. The sentry must have heard. Seconds became minutes. Either the man was in a deep sleep or the generator had masked the sound. Fraser continued towards the small opening.

It was narrower than he had at first thought: barely four feet across. He thrust his head and shoulders inside. Darkness. Then, so faint it took him several seconds to be sure, a glimmer. The vertical shaft dropped down some way to where there seemed to be an opening, leading off at almost a right angle. He took a rolled cord from his pocket, tied a stone to it and lowered it to the bottom of the shaft. Having retrieved it, he measured its length against the distance from his fingertip to his shoulder. The shaft was over twenty-five feet deep. He cut off a four-foot length of the cord to make a sling for the AK and slung it across his chest. Swinging his legs across the opening, he planted his feet on the opposite wall and, bracing his back against the wall behind him, began to inch downwards by first shifting his feet then supporting his weight with his hands and sliding his back.

His head dipped below the opening of the shaft. The first pitch was easy, but then the gap between the walls widened and with every foot he descended it became harder and harder to keep a grip on the rock with his boots. Before long he found himself almost at full stretch, his shoulders pressed against one wall, his feet barely touching the other. The sides of the shaft were almost smooth. His feet slipped and lost their purchase. He hung suspended by his outstretched arms.

By rocking his body backwards and forwards he gained enough momentum to swing his legs up, but his toes barely scraped the facing wall. He looked down. It still seemed a long way to the bottom of the shaft. The pressure of supporting his own dead weight felt like it was tearing his shoulders out of their sockets. He took two deep breaths and released his grip.

He kept his feet and knees together and his arms up. He hit the base of the shaft and immediately rolled, absorbing the shock with his whole body.

Scrambling to his feet, he found a horizontal shaft about twenty feet long which started wide but then narrowed. A dull glow lit up the far end, which looked to be barely a couple of feet wide. He dropped on to his back and went down the shaft head first, pushing with his feet and squirming with his shoulders. By the time he was halfway along it he could no longer use his legs to propel him.

He rested, his breath now coming in short gasps. At this point the tunnel was at its narrowest. The rifle slung on his chest scraped the roof above him with every movement. Sweat rolled down his face, making his eyes and nose itch. He desperately wanted to rub them but didn't have enough space to raise his arms. As he continued to writhe from side to side, his progress could now be measured in fractions of an inch. He closed his eyes against the stinging sweat. When he opened them again he was looking up into open space.

Two more minutes of frantic wriggling and he was able to sit up. He spent a satisfying minute scratching every itch on his body. He could now see clearly. The glow he had detected at the tunnel entrance was a bright artificial light. He was in a narrow cavern, its roof a good five feet from the floor on which he was sitting, its sides widening out into several other tunnels. The light was coming from the one directly ahead.

He shuffled forward at a crouch. Rounding the bend, he realized why there was only one guard at the main entrance. A metal grid had been hammered into the rock shaft. The bars were at least an inch thick, criss-crossing each other every foot or so. Looking beyond the grid, he could see a large, well-lit shaft. He tested the grid by pulling at it with all his strength. The bars were as solid as the rock walls. Perhaps more so.

Dropping to his stomach, he checked the cavern floor. The grid was supported by two massive solid circular posts which had been drilled into the rock, leaving a gap of about three inches between the bottom of the grid and the floor of the cave. A huge rock was set in the floor, next to the left-hand post. If he could remove that he might be able to crawl under the grid. He grasped the protruding edges of the rock and heaved, but there was no movement. Then he pulled his knife and chipped at the concrete into which the pole had been set. Twenty minutes later he had removed a fist-sized chunk from between the pole and the rock. When he pulled at the rock again there was the slightest give. He continued hacking at the surrounding concrete and rock with increased energy, the dull throb of the generator masking the noise.

After an hour of pulling and chipping he braced his back against the tunnel wall and placed both feet against the rock. He kicked out, using his leg and back muscles to their full. The rock yielded slightly. He gritted his teeth and shoved harder, feeling the bite of the rock face against his back. Sweat poured down his face, the pain burned through his knees and ankles. He realized that if his foot slipped he would break his ankle. Without warning the rock moved, and he began to lever it slowly out of the ground. He stopped kicking and shoved his hands underneath it and rolled it away from the base of the grid, leaving a hole eighteen inches deep.

He dug a little further, removing loose rocks and mud until he again hit solid rock. After removing his jacket, he shoved it and the AK under the grid, then turned on to his stomach and inched forward, keeping his arms in front of him, pushing with his feet and squirming with his stomach, occasionally using his hands and elbows. He found that by breathing out, moving and breathing again while resting he could make slow but sustained progress.

Once his chest was through, his legs followed easily. He stood and stretched to his full height. As he pulled on his jacket he reflected that he had learned something else about himself. He might not know who he was but he was definitely not claustrophobic.

He advanced along the tunnel, his rifle held in both hands, his finger alongside the trigger, the butt against his shoulder, ready to snap it up for a quick, accurate shot. The light gradually increased and ahead of him he could see a junction with a larger tunnel. This he approached with caution, pausing to kneel and peep around the corner. He was greeted by a sight of awesome beauty.

The tunnel connected with a large cavern. From its limestone roof long, thin straw stalactites hung down in intricate formations. A long line of naked electric lights made the stalactites shimmer in countless hues. He looked to his right, where the electric lights disappeared down a long and winding passageway, then he dropped to the ground and followed them. For the next twenty minutes he followed the lights ever downwards, through a mesh of stalactites and slightly broader stalagmites pushing up to meet them. Some of the stalactites were as thin as a single drop of rain water, and glittered like strands of living light.

He heard the thudding of the generator ahead of him and now too the sound of running water. Stepping round a tight bend, he found himself in an even more gigantic cave. He couldn't see the ceiling, but a stream of murky water flowed through an arched opening in the wall of rock. The artificial lights reflected off a six-foot-high diesel generator, which pounded out its ceaseless beat. Near by was a metal construction that he couldn't quite make out. He looked around him: all was still. He waded across the stream carefully, even though it was only a couple of feet deep.

The US Army generator was extremely powerful. The metal construction beside it was an enormous tripod with a wire cage suspended beneath it. He walked slowly towards this. Below the cage was an opening in the cave floor which was some fifteen feet in diameter. He edged nearer and looked down into blackness. Then he picked up a stone, dropped it and started to count. He reached ten before he heard the faintest of cracks.

Two thick metal hawsers guided the cage into the chasm. He studied the engineering with interest. A black rubber-encased box with two buttons, red and green, was bolted to the side of the cage. He stepped inside, pulled the metal rod into place, took a deep breath and pressed the green button.

As he dropped, almost silently, down the shaft he noticed a drill hole in the rock and, after about twenty feet, another. When a third appeared he pressed the red button and studied the hole closely. All three holes were linked by a thick white plastic wire. The entire shaft was rigged for demolition. He restarted the lift and saw more charges as it descended. It bumped gently to a halt opposite a further series of large tunnel entrances, two of which were lit.

Stepping out on to a well-prepared reception area, he looked back up the lift shaft. He couldn't see the top. He tried to estimate how deep he was. Several hundred feet at least, he decided. Someone had gone to a considerable amount of time, effort and expense here. But why?

He looked at the two illuminated tunnels, tossed a mental coin and followed the right-hand one. From the raised wooden platform at the base of the lift shaft the tunnel sloped steeply downwards and he had to grip the sides for support as he followed its winding path. It must have dropped at least another fifty feet before it began to level out. Ahead of him he saw a solid wall of rock and what looked like a smaller tunnel, but as he got closer he realized he was wrong. Rocks and rubble were heaped beside the opening. This was no accident of nature. Someone had blasted this cavern out of solid rock. He stepped inside and found himself in a hollow about fifteen feet deep by ten feet high. The walls were grey and smooth and felt relatively soft. He stepped back to the entrance and peered closely at the union between the rock and the grey material. The walls were covered with lead. As he stepped outside the metal box he realized he was walking over a smooth surface and squatted to take a closer look. Two immense sheets of lead were stacked one on top of the other, each at least four inches thick.

He shook his head and walked back to the main corridor, where four long wooden boxes caught his eye. He pulled the lid off one and found plastic containers labelled 'C4 Plastic Explosive', along with non-electrical detonators, safety fuses and rolls of white detonation cord. He gave a low whistle, then looked again at the entrance to the lead-lined chamber. A series of deep holes had been bored into the roof and side. This too had been prepared for demolition. He dropped the explosive package back into the wooden box and resealed it. As he looked around he realized that the tunnel was a dead end, so he retraced his steps.

He arrived back at the lift and considered going back up. Then he looked again at the second tunnel. So far all he had discovered were questions without answers. He turned left and began to follow it. Behind him, unseen and unheard, the cage began to ascend.

Galbraith was barely able to concentrate on the road ahead of him. He sucked heavily on the cigarette clamped between his teeth and blew a cloud of smoke at the window. He had telephoned Superintendent Johnstone immediately after Mungo Campbell had given him the results of the post-mortem. His superior's reply had stunned him. 'It's far too early to say whether or not there had been foul play. You must proceed with caution,' he had said. The fact that Johnstone himself would now oversee the investigation only rubbed salt into his wounds.

As he jerked the wheel angrily to the right to negotiate a particularly sharp turn, the wheels screamed in protest. He dropped into third gear and accelerated through the bend. Before joining the CID he had been one of the best pursuit drivers in the Glasgow force. The road levelled out and he snapped the gear lever back into fourth, driving by instinct.

He was certain Anne had been murdered; someone had poured that whisky into her. If necessary he would take the case all the way up to the Chief Constable. Another corner loomed ahead of him and this time he dropped into third in plenty of time. A picture of Anne, her neck twisted to one side, flashed into his mind. Tears welled as he tried to obliterate the image, only to have it transmute into a tangle of memories of their time together.

Anne, her face lit by candlelight, laughing at his stories. The first time they'd made love: better than anything before or since. The way she had lain afterwards, her head on his arm, idly tugging at the hairs on his chest, talking incessantly about everything and nothing. Anne jumping for joy when he'd told her he'd been promoted. Anne crying over some silly bit in a movie. Anne telling him it was over.

Again he saw her lying cold on the slab, her neck horribly contorted. Into his troubled mind came the image of a figure forcing whisky down Anne's throat, making her protest, then cough and vomit. Tears rolled down the side of his face.

'Anne,' he cried softly, shaking his head from side to side to repel his obscene imaginings of her last few minutes of life. The pictures wouldn't fade. He knew she had died in fear, in pain, without hope. Anger and hatred such as he'd never known surged through him: anger at Hamilton for taking his Anne away, hatred of the monsters who had so pitilessly destroyed her. Through clenched teeth he snarled, 'You bastards. I'll get you,' and stamped down on the accelerator.

The road ahead, lit only by the reflections from the Cat's-eyes, twisted into the night. In the distance he could see the glow of Bannock's lights against the pitch-black sky. Normally he would feel the warmth of their welcome, but tonight there was only rage in his heart.

A shape stumbled across the road in front of him. He trod down hard on the brakes. The car went into an immediate skid, but he turned into it and then out again, regaining partial control. The rear end hit the steep bank that ran alongside the right-hand side of the road with a jarring thud, throwing his head against the side window. Still he fought for control of the skidding car and brought it to a controlled stop. Leaning forward and resting his head on the steering wheel, he breathed deeply and rapidly. He unfastened his seat belt and got out, the cold night air hitting his face and helping to revive him.

There was a scurrying noise to his left. He looked around. A sheep observed him haughtily from the side of the bank. He crossed to the other side of the road and looked down. The ground fell away into the darkness.

He spun on his heels and looked back. Even in this light the skid marks were visible against the grey tarmac. He had skidded only twenty yards or so and the tyre marks were all over the road. He had reacted the way all police drivers were taught: to steer into the skid, then out of it. The marks on the road at the Devil's Horseshoe had been two long, thin, black lines burnt into the surface over some fifty yards.

Hamilton was a police driver. Even drunk he would have reacted instinctively and tried to steer his way out of a skid. Unless he had been unconscious before the crash.

10

Galbraith eased himself into his car and drove on slowly towards Bannock. He parked outside his flat and walked round to Main Street. After looking up the hill towards the police station, where Johnstone would be waiting for him, he checked his watch and decided his superior could wait a little longer. He needed a drink.

He stepped into the Marquis, ordered a double Glenfiddich and sipped it slowly, leaning on the bar. Finlay MacDonald spotted him and sidled along the other side to join him.

'You look like hell, man. What's wrong?'

'Bloody sheep ran in front of the car as I was coming back into town,' he replied, massaging his eyes. 'Made me skid off the road.'

MacDonald took his glass from his hand and added another large whisky before sliding the glass back across the bar. 'On the house, Ian,' he said with a wink.

Galbraith accepted the offer gratefully and gulped down half the measure.

The landlord rested both arms on the bar and leant towards him. 'Those sheep are a menace. Only last year Dougie MacCallister hit one on his way back from Inverness. Totally wrecked his car and he was lucky to escape with only a broken arm. You sure you're OK now?'

Absorbed with his own thoughts, Galbraith nodded absent-mindedly. Sensing the policeman wanted to be alone, Mac-Donald prepared to busy himself elsewhere, when a sudden thought struck him.

'Your lady friend . . .'

Galbraith stared at him blankly. 'What?'

'Your lady friend, the one you met in here yesterday.'

'You mean Anne?'

'Aye, that's the lady. Very nice too, if you don't mind me saying so.'

Galbraith closed his eyes. 'She's dead . . . The accident up at the Devil's Horseshoe.'

MacDonald's smile faded as he reached across to clasp Galbraith's hand. 'I'm so sorry, Ian. I had no idea she was involved.' A look of confusion flashed across his face. 'But she told me she was going straight back to Glasgow.'

'Are you sure?'

'Aye, she even asked me the time of the next bus. That's when she left this for you.'

MacDonald reached behind the bar and brought out a sealed white envelope. Galbraith's name was scrawled in black ink on the front in Anne's unmistakable handwriting.

'Pushed it across the bar and left before I could even say a word.'

MacDonald saw the look of complete sorrow on the other man's face. 'I'll be leaving you alone to read your letter, Ian . . .'

Galbraith hardly heard him. He ripped the envelope open and began to read.

Dear Ian,
    Brian's asked me to contact you and arrange a

meeting. He believes the phones in your station are bugged, so I thought I'd write this note before I left and leave it with the landlord.

Brian says he has proof your Superintendent Johnstone has been taking money from Braxton Industries. He also thinks a man named Carter was killed on the estate a few days ago. Brian thinks something really evil is happening in McLeod House. He's heard the Americans talking about an Operation Hades. He doesn't know what it's about, but whatever it is, it's going to happen soon.

Brian says to be very careful who you trust, Braxton has friends everywhere, Ministry of Defence, MI5, police, everywhere. He's especially terrified of a man named Kirby who runs the security at McLeod House. He wants you to arrange for protection for us, in return he'll give evidence against Braxton.

Brian can't risk contacting you direct. I'm going back to Glasgow today. Ring me at my father's house as soon as you get this letter. Ian – I'm so scared, please call soon.

Anne

Galbraith lit a cigarette, reread the letter and noticed with fascination that his hand was trembling.

'You've got blood just above your right eye,' said a soft voice.

Charlotte Reynolds was standing next to him. He folded the letter quickly then touched his forehead and looked at the smear of blood on his fingers. 'Sheep ran out in front of me, sent me into a skid.'

She observed him coolly. 'You were lucky. What about the other accident?'

Galbraith turned back to the bar. 'Inquiries are still ongoing.'

She studied his profile. 'I had an interesting talk with Mr Kirby yesterday. You know him, of course?'

Galbraith's mind was elsewhere: thinking about his coming confrontation with Johnstone and Hamilton's warning that his own superintendent was taking money from Braxton. He missed the hard tone in her voice. 'I've never met the man . . . Seen him about once or twice.'

'I see,' she said quietly.

'Why all this interest in Kirby?' Galbraith turned, but she had gone. He shrugged, folded Anne's letter neatly and put it in his pocket. After finishing his whisky he left the pub and began the walk up the hill to the station. As soon as he stepped into his own office Johnstone sprang up and snapped, 'Just what in heaven's name is this all about, Chief Inspector? You ring demanding we open a murder investigation and then become abusive when I tell you it's too early to say whether or not there's been foul play.'

Galbraith sat opposite the Superintendent. 'Anne and Brian Hamilton were murdered,' he said flatly. 'You want proof, here it is.' He reached for a buff-coloured file and threw it on to the desktop.

Johnstone picked it up hesitantly and began to read.

'Keep going. The conclusion is most enlightening,' Galbraith told him.

Johnstone stiffened. He glanced at Galbraith and back to the report. 'This can't be true.' There was genuine horror in his voice.

'It's true. There is no way, no way whatsoever, that Anne would have drunk that much.'

Johnstone shook his head. 'Perhaps somebody spiked her drinks as a joke?'

Galbraith massaged his brow. He waited a few seconds before replying, knowing he had to keep control of himself. 'Sir, no matter how the alcohol was administered, after one, two drinks at the very most, Anne would have been convulsed with pain. She had the equivalent of half a bottle inside her. Somebody poured it into them both.'

'But why?'

'Anne spoke to me before she died, told me that Brian was in some kind of difficulty over at Braxton's. She said that he was in real danger and that her phone had been tapped.'

'Had she any idea why Hamilton might be in danger?'

Galbraith thought of the letter in his pocket and decided to play his cards very close to his chest. Perhaps if he gave Johnstone enough rope he would hang himself.

'No, but she was right, wasn't she? And there's another thing. The skid marks on the road are long and straight. It didn't register until I nearly had a smash myself this evening, but Brian was police-trained: he would have tried to steer his way out of trouble. Even if he'd had a skinful he would have at least tried.'

Johnstone was white. 'We've never had a murder investigation in this division in all my time here.'

'Well, you've got one now, sir,' Galbraith replied.

Johnstone nodded and lapsed into a long silence.

'How many people know about this?'

'Just you, me and Mungo Campbell.'

'Let's keep it like that. I don't want this place awash with rumours. We must proceed with caution, Ian. Braxton is a very important man. I'll inform the Chief Constable personally and conduct preliminary interviews on the Braxton estate. You concentrate on this end. See if you can trace Mrs Hamilton's movements after she left you.'

'I'll get right on it.' Galbraith was already half out of his seat.

'Tomorrow will be fine, Ian. You look dead beat and there's still blood on . . .'

'I'd rather make a start . . .'

'Ian, we both know that when a man's tired he misses things.' He leaned over to tap Galbraith's arm. 'Now off you go and get some rest.'

Galbraith nodded. 'You're right. I'll make a start tomorrow.'

'Good man,' Johnstone said. 'I think I'll stay here and look through this file in a little more detail.'

When Galbraith had gone Johnstone waited for five minutes, then lifted the phone and dialled. When it was answered he said quietly, 'This is Superintendent Johnstone. Tell Mr Braxton I need to speak to him urgently.'

Kirby and Gunn arrived at the potholes and made radio contact with the sentries, who reported nothing suspicious. Kirby wasn't convinced.

'You stay here, Leo, and take a look around. I'll go meet the boys. We'll work our way in toward you.'

Gunn nodded once in reply and watched as Kirby climbed into his Range Rover and drove off. After looking carefully along the edge of the escarpment he walked a little way inside the entrance. There he found the sentry sitting on a folding chair, reading a Western novel and wearing a pair of red plastic ear defenders. Reaching forward, he pulled them off. The man looked up, startled.

'Oh, it's you, Mr Gunn.'

Duane Sanson was one of the youngest members of the security team. His face showed a mixture of surprise and apprehension as he stared up into Gunn's face. The ear defenders dangled from the big man's meaty paw.

'It's that damn generator, Mr Gunn. The noise drives me crazy,' murmured the sentry, his face reddening under the other man's withering stare.

Gunn tossed the ear defenders aside and leaned forward to make himself heard.

'I'm gonna have a look inside. You stay here and keep alert.' His voice was surprisingly soft.

'Sure thing, Mr Gunn.'

With a final look of disdain Gunn made his way down the lit passage. He waded across the stream to the generator. Suddenly he stopped. Something was wrong. The cage was down. He walked to the shaft and peered over the rails. Then he reached for the control pad and pressed the recall button. Above his head the lift mechanism kicked into life.

Water seeped down the sides of the tunnel, glistening in the glare from the unshielded electric lights above. In one place the left-hand wall disappeared completely to reveal a gaping chasm. Fraser stopped to look over the edge but his eyes couldn't penetrate the darkness.

Ahead of him, from behind a tight right-hand bend, the light grew brighter. He found himself in another chamber. On the floor were six long, black plastic bags. He knew exactly what they were. Propping his rifle against the cavern wall, he dropped to his knees and unzipped the first.

He recognized the face immediately. It was the man he had shot when he had decided to re-enter the woods. He zipped up the bag and opened the next. It held the Indian who had been tracking him. The third revealed the Mexican he had killed in the knife fight on the first day.

The next one contained the body of a man whose face he vaguely recognized. He was in his early thirties and had been shot twice, once in the chest and once in the mouth. His face was handsome even in death. Its owner looked intelligent and his clothes were expensive. That face haunted Fraser. He knew it was important. He reached for it in his memory, but it was gone.

The occupant of the next bag was a giant of a man. The face was hard and flat, with slanting eyes and high cheekbones. From somewhere deep inside Fraser a wave of almost uncontrollable anger swept over him. He wanted to smash that face, obliterate it. Instead he took several deep breaths, and control gradually returned. He unzipped the bag further to check for bullet or knife wounds. Nothing. The man must have weighed a good seventeen stone.

As his fingers touched the zip of the last bag, he paused. He didn't want to do this. His hands recoiled from the cold plastic. Then he reached forward again, his heart beating faster, and cautiously drew down the heavy zip. Through the slit he could see the outline of a soft, feminine face. His stomach heaved and hot bile burned the back of his throat. With sudden urgency he reached forward and pulled the bag apart. His cry of anguish echoed through the cave. He rocked back on his heels, tears coursing down his face.

Gunn stepped from the lift and looked at the two tunnels. He had a fifteen-shot 9mm Beretta in a shoulder holster but didn't bother to draw it. He wanted to finish this man with his bare hands. When he was fourteen he'd killed his first man that way: a New Orleans pimp who took all his mother's money and beat her every Saturday night. He had strangled him in his sleep and enjoyed watching the man's eyes bulge as he fought for air. During his time in Delta Force he had become a master of silent killing. Now he was looking forward to some practice.

Gunn was heading towards the right-hand tunnel and the lead-lined reception chamber when a faint, animal cry stopped him in his tracks. He knew what had caused that cry. Turning sharply, he headed down the left-hand tunnel, with no more sound than a passing shadow.

How long Fraser sat there looking at her face he couldn't tell; it could have been a minute or an hour. His mind was numb. Almost involuntarily, he reached across to touch her face. Even in death she looked so beautiful. A name forced its way to his lips. 'Lindsey Fraser.'

Other memories started to fill his mind. Memories of . . . He froze. Whether he heard something or merely sensed it, he didn't know. He leapt to his feet and turned to face the cave's entrance. Framed there was Gunn.

Fraser's eyes darted to the rifle propped against the wall – it was too far away. The huge man followed his gaze, his lips parted in a smile, a gold-capped tooth glinting in the artificial light. He wagged his index finger slowly, as if to scold Fraser for having naughty thoughts.

Fraser's Browning was in the shoulder holster under his left arm. He cursed himself for having zipped up his jacket. With a short step to the left, he edged away from the body bags and then stopped, his left leg forward, knees slightly bent, weight balanced on the balls of his feet. He kept his hands open and low, ready to strike or grapple.

Gunn watched his every move, noted the combat stance,

then started to move towards him, his hands high and open, shoulders' breadth apart. Fraser never took his eyes off those massive hands. Gunn advanced silkily on the balls of his feet, always moving his left leg first, to maintain his balance. He paused again, just out of striking range, his dark eyes taking in every detail.

His attack was appallingly fast. Stepping forward briskly, he launched two ferocious straight jabs, following them with a low roundhouse kick. Fraser sensed rather than saw the punches coming; he blocked one and took the second on the left shoulder. The kick smashed into the left side of his ribcage and, although the holstered Browning helped protect him, the impact threw him across the cavern. He landed heavily on one of the body bags and rolled away just in time to avoid a stamp on the throat that would have finished him. Lying on his back, he kicked out with his right foot and felt a savage glee as his boot heel caught the other man just below the knee. Gunn gave a grunt of pain as his leg collapsed underneath him.

Fraser rolled away and sprang to his feet, only to find that his opponent was already up and lunging straight at him. They closed, Gunn's momentum and greater weight forcing Fraser back against the cavern wall. This sudden giving of ground threw Gunn momentarily off balance and Fraser seized the opportunity to thrust his right hand forward with the thumb extended. It entered the other man's left eye socket almost up to the knuckle, making him throw his head back with a scream of agony.

Gunn's anger almost consumed him. He would destroy the man that had hurt him. His huge fists struck out in a frenzy. Fraser fought back, smashing blows into his stomach. It was like punching an iron wall. All skills were forgotten as each man fought with an almost primeval intensity. Most of Gunn's punches missed or were glancing blows, but those that landed solidly were like sledgehammers. Fraser couldn't take much more punishment. Gunn sensed him weakening and gave a howl of triumph as he redoubled his attack.

Fraser stopped punching and brought his hands up to protect his head and upper body. He moved from side to side to ride the terrible assault. Gunn leaned back to get better leverage. It was what Fraser had hoped for. He threw both his legs out, landing with a bump on his backside. For a second he was sitting directly below Gunn. He punched upwards with every ounce of his remaining strength, driving his fist two inches into Gunn's unprotected groin.

Air exploded from the man's lungs; pain too awful to bear overwhelmed him. His knees gave away and he found himself looking into the eyes of the man he had been so confident of killing. He saw no mercy in them.

Measuring his distance, Fraser drew in a huge gulp of air and struck again, his right hand open and rigid, powered by all the force of his arms and shoulders. The curve between his thumb and fingers slammed into the kneeling man's unprotected throat. The sombre eyes bulged. Fraser leaned back against the wall, watching, at the end of his strength.

Gunn stayed where he was for several seconds then toppled sideways. For perhaps a further twenty seconds he remained conscious, trying to force air into his lungs through the shattered windpipe. Even after all conscious thought had gone his body twitched for several minutes as first the heart, then the nervous system and finally the brain ceased to function.

Fraser got slowly to his feet. Every inch of him hurt. His left eye was already swelling and felt like it was about to close altogether. He wanted nothing more than to lie down and sleep for a lifetime. He staggered to the cave's entrance and picked up the AK. Holding it in both hands, he made his way unsteadily along the tunnel to the lift shaft.

He stepped into the cage, closed it and pressed the button. As the lift started its clanking ascent he took three deep breaths, then slipped the magazine off the rifle and checked it. Fifteen rounds left. After reloading it, he checked the Browning inside his jacket. He expected to find a welcoming committee at the top of the shaft. How many of them, he didn't know – and at that moment he didn't care.

As the top supporting girders of the hoist appeared above him, Fraser pulled the butt of the AK47 tight into his shoulder, twisted the stock and pistol grip towards each other to steady the weapon and crouched in the classic combat stance. He could pivot and fire in any direction while presenting the smallest possible target. The lift jolted to a halt under the massive tripod. Fraser whirled in a fluid arc as he checked the area. Nothing. Surely the black guy had not been alone.

He began to retrace his steps towards the exit when he heard the murmur of voices. They became louder. At least half a dozen men were heading towards him.

He raced back to the cage and was about to step in when he halted. As the lift descended he would be trapped. Several smaller caves branched off from the main cavern. Choosing one at random, he took three steps inside. The darkness closed around him. He settled down to wait and watch.

A group of men splashed through the stream, heading towards him. Leading them was Kirby, an MP5 Kurtz in one hand. The vicious little sub-machine-gun had a double thirty-round magazine. The security chief glanced around, threw back his head and shouted Gunn's name. Then he turned to the man standing beside him. 'How long ago did you say he came in here?'

'Must have been a good half-hour ago, Mr Kirby,' Duane Sanson answered, his eyes darting nervously around the chamber.

Kirby threw back his head again and yelled, 'Leo! Goddamn you, Leo. Where the hell are you?' The words echoed off the walls.

Kirby turned to Weaver. 'Take four men and go back to the entrance. I want you to check the side tunnels again – the ones we sealed off when we began this thing. The rest of you spread out and look for Leo. And be careful.'

The six men, weapons at the ready, extended their line and began to sweep towards the lift. Kirby controlled the line from the centre, using hand signals to move three men forward at a time, so that the others could give them immediate and concentrated covering fire. They reached the lift and spread out in an arc, each man taking cover, weapon in the shoulder, while Kirby pondered the situation.

'Mr Kirby.'

He looked up to see Weaver running towards him so fast that the three men following could hardly keep up.

'Fraser's here, Mr Kirby. Inside the cavern complex. We found the place where he crawled under an iron grid to get in.'

'Any chance he could have gotten back out the same way?'

'Not a chance. The crawl marks all lead one way. He's still inside.'

'Sam, take your three men down to the lower chambers. Be careful. All of you stay together and search each tunnel in turn. Only one man moving at any one time, OK?'

'Got you, Mr Kirby.'

Kirby paced backwards and forwards as the minutes dragged by. Suddenly the noise of the lift ascending broke the rhythmic hum of the generator. Everyone turned to look towards the grim, angry faces of the four men as the cage slid into view.

Weaver walked purposefully towards the security chief. 'Leo's dead. We found him in the chamber with the body bags.'

Kirby's eyes closed for a second and his body shook slightly. 'How?'

'It looks like he crushed his windpipe.'

'With his bare hands?'

'Looks that way, Mr Kirby.'

Kirby grimaced. 'I've had enough of this shit. Fraser's up here in one of those three tunnels. The lift was in the "up" position when we arrived and he hasn't gotten back out the way he came in. No,' – he paused and stared intently at the three tunnels in turn – 'he's in one of them.'

Fraser shivered slightly. He would have preferred the security chief to rant and rave. An angry man loses his sense of reason.

Kirby pulled his radio from his belt. 'Frank, this is Matt. Over.'

'Roger, Mr Kirby.'

'Bring in your people and the night gear.'

'Roger. Out.'

Five minutes later six more men carrying two large canvas bags between them joined those already in front of him.

Kirby addressed his team. 'Sam, Frank. You got the maps of the tunnel complex?'

Both men nodded.

'Good. Remember they're not complete but they'll give

you an idea of the ground we have to search. Some of the tunnels haven't been fully investigated and some could lead back up to the surface. That's why we're going in after him. OK?'

'We want him as bad as you, Mr Kirby,' Weaver growled.

'Keep cool, Sam. He wants us to lose our heads.'

'Yessir, Mr Kirby.'

'Right.' Kirby raised his voice slightly to ensure everybody heard him. 'We'll split into four teams of four. Frank, pick your men from the group you had outside and take them into that tunnel. Sam, you take the middle one and I'll take the far left. The rest will remain here as a stopper force. Remember, two men move, two men cover. Keep your moving time short. We're in no hurry to get this turkey. I don't have to remind you how dangerous he can be. Now, there's a lot of side passages and some connect. Be sure to check them all, and don't stray into another complex. We don't want any friendly fire. OK, let's gear up.'

Fraser noted the speed and discipline with which they formed into groups. He watched them strap infrared torches to their weapons. From the bags they produced sets of goggles. Fraser recognized them and cursed. They were I-MAC image-intensifiers, or passive night goggles, designed for pilots and special forces. With these and the infrared torches on their weapons, the darkened tunnels would seem as bright as daylight to his pursuers.

He retreated down the tunnel as fast as he could. When he was sure he couldn't be seen from the entrance he switched on his torch and made better progress. He knew he could neither outrun nor hide from Kirby's men. He had to think of an answer – fast.

McLeod House was unusually quiet, Superintendent Johnstone thought, as he pulled up at the imposing entrance. He crunched across the gravel but turned as he heard the screech of a hunting night owl. His ancestors had always considered it a bad omen. Behind him the heavy oak door opened, bathing him in light. Braxton stood alone in the doorway.

'Good evening, Superintendent. Glad you could come.'

'You didn't leave me a lot of choice.'

Braxton smiled. 'You sounded as if you were panicking, Superintendent. We don't want things getting out of hand.'

'Out of hand? Two people are dead, maybe murdered. What else has to happen before things get out of hand?'

Braxton stilled the outburst with an upraised hand. 'All your questions will be answered shortly.'

'It's not just me. Chief Inspector Galbraith is like a pit bull. Once he gets his teeth into something like this he just won't let go.'

'I'm sure we can sort everything out, Superintendent. Come into the study.'

Johnstone followed Braxton into the deserted hallway. On his previous visits the place had been crawling with security personnel.

'Where is everybody?'

Braxton stopped, his hand on the study door. 'We're running a major security exercise in the northern woods. Matt Kirby has every available man involved.'

Johnstone studied his face. The smile was still in place but he could sense something behind the eyes. Worry, fear? It was there and then gone. Whatever was happening it had nothing to do with exercise. Perhaps it had been a mistake to come here after all. He tried to convince himself that it had nothing to do with the job that Braxton had offered him, and almost succeeded.

Braxton stepped to one side and Johnstone hesitated as he saw a figure seated next to the roaring fire. 'You haven't met, gentlemen. Sir Marcus Brown, Permanent Under Secretary of State for Industry. Superintendent Johnstone, Highlands Police.'

Sir Marcus stood and extended a hand. 'My pleasure. Edward tells me you might be coming to work for him.'

Johnstone accepted the proffered hand warily. 'Nothing's finalized yet. I'm still reviewing my options.'

'Capital.' Sir Marcus clapped him on the shoulder. 'Cautious and shrewd.' He turned to Braxton, who had settled in a spacious armchair. 'You were right to be impressed, Edward.'

Johnstone was faintly irritated. 'I'd prefer to speak in private, Mr Braxton.'

'Sir Marcus is the reason I insisted you come over this evening. You can speak openly in front of him.'

'Don't be so formal, old boy. Sit down, sit down. Have a drink,' the civil servant insisted.

Johnstone allowed himself to be ushered to an armchair and accepted the brandy that Sir Marcus thrust into his hand.

'I'm here on an official matter, Sir Marcus . . .'

'I understand perfectly, Superintendent Johnstone, and it relates to my presence here. Before I continue, please be reassured that everything said in this room is in the strictest confidence.'

'Of course.'

'Good, now let me be quite candid with you. I work for Braxton Industries, or to be more exact, I work for Edward Braxton.' Sir Marcus flashed a smile in the American's direction.

Johnstone allowed his confusion to register on his face.

'But you just said you were Permanent Under Secretary of State for Industry.'

'Oh I am, old boy, and in that capacity I prove very useful to Mr Braxton.'

Johnstone got to his feet. 'I don't think I want to hear any more.' He strode towards the door.

'What do you think your superiors would say if they were to discover that Braxton Industries had paid you £30,000?'

Johnstone paused, then turned, his face paling. 'That money was for . . .'

'I know, I know: consultation on security at McLeod House. We both know that police regulations explicitly forbid police officers from accepting payments of any kind while they are serving in the force.'

'You might also have a little difficulty explaining why it was necessary for Braxton Industries to open an account in your name in Jersey,' Braxton put in.

'That was at your suggestion,' Johnstone spluttered.

'Or why Braxton Industries needed such advice in the first place. After all, I already employ some of the finest security experts in the world.'

'You said you wanted local input.' Even to himself, Johnstone's protestation sounded weak.

'We know that, but you can see how it would look,' said Sir Marcus. He lit a cigar, and through a cloud of smoke, added, 'Please sit down again, won't you?'

Johnstone stumbled back to his chair.

'That's better,' Sir Marcus said pleasantly. 'As you're going to become one of the family, you'd better understand a little more about Braxton Industries. When Edward here inherited the family business thirty years ago, it was a relatively small concern, specializing in machine tools. In ten years he turned it into one of the top ten US firms, specializing in producing high-quality weapons for the defence industry.

'In that capacity Edward proved rather useful to organizations like the CIA and our MI6. These agencies frequently required weapons that were untraceable. Edward duly obliged, and in so doing, built up contacts in the security services of most of the Western powers.

'In the early eighties, guided by intelligence from these agencies, he was far-sighted enough to anticipate the collapse of the Soviet Union. He channelled his not inconsiderable wealth into energy, acquiring nuclear power stations in the US and developing oilfields as far apart as Alaska, South America and, more recently, the former Soviet Union itself.'

Sir Marcus paused, considering his next words carefully.

'Braxton Industries is now one of the leading energy concerns on the planet. It employs men like me, men with access to the wheels of power, all over the world. We ensure its smooth running. But now the very foundations of this multinational company are threatened.'

'And you're going to help us put things right,' Braxton said softly.

'Me, how?'

'By settling this business with your meddling Chief Inspector Galbraith,' Braxton said firmly.

'Then you can retire next year and become one of the most highly paid security chiefs in the oil industry,' Sir Marcus said persuasively. 'The alternative is at best disgrace; at worst . . .' He shrugged

'At worst,' Braxton continued for him, his voice as hard as the granite blocks of McLeod House, 'you can join the late Mr Hamilton and his wife.'

Both men watched the policeman intently. He sat with his

head lowered, staring into his untouched glass of brandy, his feet tapping a nervous tattoo on the thick pile carpet. Sir Marcus let the seconds drag out, then asked in his usual high-pitched, wheedling tones, 'Well, Superintendent Johnstone, what will it be?'

Fraser scuttled along the tunnel's twisting length, trying to put some distance between himself and his pursuers. After he had gone no more than a hundred yards or so he found the passageway narrowing. Glistening stalagmites blocked his way like silent sentinels. The tunnel floor was loose, sandy rock, so he would hear anyone approaching well in advance. He stopped, swung his torch around to get his bearings and squatted down. This was as good a place as any to make his stand.

His pursuers would only be able to come towards him one at a time. He leaned his rifle against the wall of the tunnel and switched off his torch. The darkness was all-encompassing. He couldn't see the weapon a bare two feet away. Come to that, he couldn't see his hand in front of his face.

His options were limited. Shooting in the dark, blind, was out of the question. Even if he was lucky enough to hit anything, they would see his muzzle flash and with their night goggles and infrared torches would pick him off with ease.

If he used his torch to guide his shooting it would only increase the speed with which his hunters would detect his position. He might be lucky enough to drop the point man, but before he could locate and target his back-up it would be curtains. He needed an edge.

He remembered moving in countryside lit a brilliant green. He was on a patrol outside Crossmaglen in the IRA bandit country of South Armagh.

Behind him moved three men carrying Armalite rifles and wearing, like him, single-lens passive night goggles that made them look like characters from a science-fiction film. He held up a hand and two of the men disappeared like wraiths into a hedgerow. The other man followed him into a farmyard. Inside a barn was a flatbed lorry covered by a dirty tarpaulin sheet. He climbed aboard and threw it back. A row of hollow tubes, each containing a primed mortar bomb, pointed towards the barn's low roof. Fraser gave the thumbs up to his companion and drew the sheet over the find.

They clambered down and covered each other as they moved to the double barn doors. A dog barked. Both of them paused. The dog grew more agitated. Lights came on in a distant farm house. They moved quickly back towards the road. He stumbled over a wooden fence as he became disorientated by the lack of peripheral vision and the difficulty of gauging distance. He felt the hard surface of the road under his feet and started to dart across to the other side. Without warning, a car rounded a corner, its engine drowned out by the dog's barking. He stood in the middle of the road, like a startled rabbit caught in a car's headlights. Everything suddenly went black, as the night goggles blanked out, unable to cope with the bright light. He ran across the road blindly, one hand reaching up to tear them off.

He stepped into a ditch on the other side and fell headlong into the arms of his cover man. The car sped past, unaware of their presence. In the barn across the road, men with rifles and torches were searching around the outside of the barn. He felt his hand being grasped and he was led by his cover man into the safety of the night.

An idea took shape in his mind. He switched on his torch and removed the steel mug from the water bottle on his belt. From his survival kit he took out two boxes of matches, kept three and emptied the rest into the mug. Now he had to make a decision: the AK or the Browning. He decided on the automatic pistol as it was more effective in the narrow confines of the tunnel, so he pulled the rifle towards him, ejected the round in the chamber and emptied the magazine. With his knife he levered the heads off the rounds and poured the contents into the mug. He worked fast: he had little time.

Frank led his small team along the tunnel in a silent 'fire and manoeuvre' action. Two men knelt, their weapons in their shoulders, while the other two moved. Each pair travelled in tactical bounds, never more than ten yards, before kneeling and allowing the two rear men to stand up and move past them.

Then Frank held up his hand and the other three froze. The passageway ahead narrowed. It would be a good place for an ambush. Frank turned his head slowly from left to right, illuminating the passage in an ethereal green light, the beam from his infrared torch on his rifle projecting a bright shaft of light invisible to the naked eye. He moved his rifle left and right, the torch beam reflecting a more brilliant green as it shimmered over the stalactites. He could detect no danger. He held up one finger. His cover man closed up on him, while the other two members of his patrol remained where they were.

Frank began to edge forward, gripping the butt of his AK47 tight against his shoulder and swinging its slightly lowered barrel in short, swift arcs, searching for a target. Aiming a rifle was difficult when wearing night goggles, but he knew that if he placed a cross on a target his rounds would land within an inch or two of it.

His cover man followed six feet behind him, the two of them moving in synchronized slow motion, a macabre silent dance, with death as a partner, just waiting to cut in. Frank kicked a rock and muttered to himself. It was damn difficult moving when you couldn't see your feet. He looked down and saw Fraser's discarded AK. He was just raising his head when his night goggles registered a sudden burst of light.

Fraser had tied the mug to one of the stalactites at about head height and had deliberately left the AK lying on the ground, wanting something to halt and distract his pursuers. When he heard Frank he knew they were close enough. He struck the three matches, the flare of their ignition causing Frank and his cover man to peer in his direction. Even as Frank's finger curled round the trigger of his rifle Fraser dropped the matches into the mug. The effect was startling.

With a sudden, blinding flash, the phosphorus and cordite ignited. The goggles' sophisticated light filters couldn't cope, leaving Frank and his cover man momentarily sightless. Frank fired, his shots going high right. Behind him his cover man held his fire, unsure where his leader was.

Fraser held the Browning in one hand, his torch in the other. He flicked the torch on and fired two rounds. Without pausing to confirm whether or not his shots had struck home he pivoted slightly and caught the cover man trying desperately to rip off his goggles. Fraser fired again: a double tap. The two 9mm rounds, travelling at just under a thousand feet per second, hit the man just below his right eye, blowing a hole as big as a saucer out of the back of his head.

Fraser clicked off his torch and dropped to his knees. He could see nothing but could not risk using it again. He knew there were at least two more men close by. He could hear their shouts and knew he had only seconds to do what he had to.

He edged towards Frank's body. His hands found the feet

and groped swiftly upwards, at once becoming wet and sticky. One of his rounds had hit the man in the chest, the other in the throat. He ripped the goggles off the dead man's head and slipped them over his own, just as he heard the sound of approaching footsteps.

The goggles were returning to normal: the flash from his 'smudge' bomb had caused only a momentary loss of focus. He could see clearly for twenty yards and brought the Browning up in both hands.

'Frank. You OK, buddy?'

The voice was a low, urgent whisper. It was the first unprofessional thing he'd seen his hunters do. Coming forward into a contact and calling out was just asking for trouble. He grunted something unintelligible.

'Frank, is that you?'

The man appeared. Fraser sighted and fired four times in quick succession, then stood up and ran, doubled over, towards him. He was just reaching for the downed man's Heckler & Koch sub-machine-gun when he came under heavy fire. Snatching it up, he rolled backwards.

For two or three seconds the stalactites around him were smashed to smithereens. Only inches from his face he could see the impact of the rounds against the wall. Rock chips sprayed, cutting his face like a sand blaster. He hardly heard the noise, but was acutely aware of the stink of cordite. He tried to roll faster, but his arms and legs were suddenly like lead. Then he heard a loud click. The firing stopped.

Fraser stood up as the man facing him frantically tried to change magazines. He held the Browning in one hand and took deliberate aim. The man slipped on a new magazine and looked up as he re-cocked his rifle. He saw Fraser standing less than ten yards from him.

'We call that "Dead man's click", pal. Should have counted your rounds.'

The man snarled something Fraser could not understand. Fraser fired twice. His eardrums reverberated from the cacophony of gunfire. In the confines of the tunnels the noise had been deafening. In its aftermath the silence was intense. For a second he remained standing, sweeping the rock face with his newly acquired goggles. Nothing moved.

He moved from body to body, collecting anything he thought he could use. He kept the Heckler & Koch, and picked up four spare thirty-round magazines. One of the cover men was carrying a Browning, so he retrieved two spare mags for his back-up weapon. He picked up a spare set of goggles and smashed the other two. He didn't know how many they had but he wasn't about to make them a present of any. In Frank's top pocket he found two American MI fragmentation grenades. They would be a dangerous weapon to use in a confined space, but he slipped them into his own pocket just in case. He also found two chocolate bars.

He saw the dead men's pale-green faces lit up in the beam of his infrared torch. Faces contorted into grimaces of pain, hatred and surprise. Frank was the oldest, probably in his early thirties. None of the other three was yet twenty-five. He suddenly felt sick. He took a deep breath and forced the emotions boiling up inside him to a far corner of his mind. Now was not the time. Now it was only kill or be killed.

He was about to move off when Frank's radio burst into life.

'Frank, this is Matt. I had a report that you hit a contact. Send me a situation report. Over. Frank, this is Matt. Come in. Over.'

Fraser picked up the radio and weighed it in his hand.

'Frank. Anybody in Frank's team, come in. This is Matt. Over.' The voice was more urgent. Fraser flicked on the send switch and spoke softly.

'Hello, Matt.'

Silence. Fraser could almost picture the look of surprise on the other man's face.

'Fraser?'

'That's right.'

There were a few seconds of silence.

'What about Frank and his patrol?'

Fraser looked at the dead bodies at his feet.

'I'm afraid they weren't up to the job.'

'You better hope we don't get you alive, buddy.'

Fraser's expression hardened.

'I don't worry about that at all. I suppose I'll be seeing you soon in person?'

'You can take that to the bank, buddy.'

'Who has a "sense of grievance" now?' He wanted the leader of his pursuers angry.

The radio remained silent. He decided to try one more time.

'What's the matter? Cat got your tongue? Your friend Leo was more talkative.'

Again silence. Then the radio went dead. Fraser took a deep breath and let it out slowly, suddenly very tired. His watch told him it was midnight, as if that meant anything in the timeless darkness of the tunnels. He considered his next move. His hunters would take time to plan and regroup. Then they would come after him in force.

He moved on, faster now with the aid of the night goggles. The tunnel changed, the shale on its floor giving way to a mass of small, sharp rocks that cut into his boots and forced him to slow his pace again. A twisted ankle would be as deadly as a bullet to him now.

The tunnel began to climb steeply and he found himself stumbling more frequently. He recognized the signs. The adrenalin surge used up his body's reserves faster than any form of physical exercise. Rest was what he needed if he was to remain alert. A tired man was prone to make mistakes and he couldn't afford even one.

He stumbled on, looking for a defensible position to lie up in. Eventually he found a massive boulder choke from where he could hold off a small army if he had to. He settled down but sleep wouldn't readily come.

He checked his watch again: one o'clock. There were no fears of them following him tonight. The man he was up against was too good a commander to push his men when they were tired, especially after the bloody nose he'd handed them. But tomorrow the security chief would come after him with a prepared plan and everything he had.

Fraser tried to put himself in the man's position. His team must try to keep him bottled up inside the tunnels. His own top priority must be to find a way out. And after that? He wanted the answer to all this, wanted it more than the air he breathed.

12

Galbraith woke to an incessant ringing. He'd drunk too many whiskies in the Marquis the night before. The dull ache in his head threatened to make him throw up and his mouth felt as if something had died in it. He moved his head slowly. The ringing continued. He opened one eye and fumbled for the phone.

'Hello.' His voice sounded awful, even to him.

'Mr Galbraith?' The night duty sergeant sounded unsure.

'Who else do you think it would be?' Galbraith retorted, focusing his eyes on the clock. 'It's five-thirty in the bloody morning, man.'

'Aye, Mr Galbraith. There's a Superintendent Melrose on the telephone, ringing from Scotland Yard. He insists that he speak to you urgently.'

Galbraith sat upright, throwing off the effects of the previous night's alcohol in an instant.

'Take a number and tell him I'll call him back in five minutes.'

'Right you are, Mr Galbraith.'

'And Sergeant, make sure that it is a Scotland Yard number before you ring me back.'

'Aye, sir.'

Galbraith swung his legs out of bed and walked unsteadily

to the kitchen. Yanking open the fridge door, he removed a bottle of lemonade and drank half of it in one go. The phone rang again. The duty sergeant recited a number and confirmed that it belonged to Scotland Yard. Galbraith slumped back down on the bed, lit a cigarette, coughed and began dialling.

'Superintendent Melrose.'

'This is Chief Inspector Galbraith, Highlands Police. I believe you wanted a word?'

'Thank you for ringing back so promptly, Chief Inspector. My apologies for the early hour.'

'Think nothing of it.' Galbraith knew from the other man's tone that he was anything but apologetic.

'I'll come straight to the point, Chief Inspector. Does the name George Carter mean anything to you?'

Galbraith recalled that Anne had mentioned a man named Carter in her letter. There was no way he was going to tell Melrose that, not over an open line. 'Can't say it does. Should it?'

'I don't know. He was a senior member of Customs and Excise with special expertise in nuclear industry material.'

'Still doesn't ring a bell.'

'I'm investigating his murder.'

Galbraith's mouth pinched. 'How was he killed?'

'Shot twice in the head at close range with a high-powered handgun. Ballistics still haven't confirmed the calibre, which isn't really surprising since there wasn't much left of his head. We only confirmed his identity from dental records.'

'When did it happen?'

'We don't know exactly. He was found three days ago in his flat in London. The place had been ransacked.'

'A burglary gone wrong?'

'That's what we were meant to think. There was extensive hypostasis to the dead man's chest and back.'

Galbraith's eyebrows rose. 'I see,' he said softly. It looked as if Hamilton had been right.

'Officially, we are still maintaining it was a bungled burglary. In fact, only the pathologist, myself – and now you – know it wasn't. For reasons I won't go into on this line, I'm keeping this investigation very low-profile.'

'Which brings you to my neck of the woods?'

'Precisely. His sister was on holiday in France but she had a phone call while in Paris.' There was a faint rustle of papers. 'He told her that he'd got himself into some sort of trouble and was going up to Bannock to sort it out.'

Galbraith picked up a pencil stub. 'What kind of car did Carter drive?'

'A black Jaguar XJ6 VRM, M259 CAG,' Melrose recited quickly. 'It was found parked outside his block of flats.'

'I'll have a quiet word – see what I can dig up.'

'I'd be obliged. I'll be in touch again.' There was a slight pause. 'Soon.' The line went dead.

Galbraith replaced the handset, dragged deep on his cigarette and breathed out a cloud of blue smoke.

'Curiouser and curiouser,' he whispered softly.

Kirby peered at his watch. Six-thirty. He had decided not to pursue Fraser during the night. He needed time to think and his men needed rest. They were stirring themselves around him with the usual bad grace of any group of soldiers, grumbling about the river-scarred rock floor and not getting enough sleep. They were holding up well, he decided, despite last night's losses. The time to worry was when they stopped bitching.

Sam Weaver had set up a makeshift field kitchen and the smell of frying eggs and bacon filled the air. Weaver brought him a steaming mess tin and he nodded his thanks. The food tasted good, but he ate mechanically, engrossed in the sketch maps of the tunnel complex. He had the outline of a plan in mind, but waited until all the men were fed before calling them round him.

'Sam, you did the recce of the tunnels when we moved in and prepared the sketch maps.'

'Sure did, Mr Kirby.'

'What's in Fraser's tunnel?'

'Partly blocked with stalactites, boulder chokes, ravines. Some water. Rough country. Whole lot of side tunnels – we ain't mapped them all.'

'And the main tunnel?'

'Easier going, but it drops steeply at the end. You'd need ropes to make any progress.'

'There's a connecting tunnel near the end here, right?' Kirby pointed to the sketch map.

'Yeah. It's a tight squeeze, but a man can get through – just.'

'Good. Take three men, travel light, get to that connecting tunnel then start back toward us. How long do you think it will take you?'

'About two hours, if we go hell for leather.'

'Do that. And set off as soon as you can.'

'What about Fraser?'

'He didn't get Frank's map. I'm surprised he missed that. I expected more from our boy. Without it he's like a rat in a maze. Don't worry about Fraser – we'll keep him busy until you get behind him.'

*

169

Half an hour later Fraser was woken by a voice in his ear.

'Fraser, you awake, buddy?'

It took him a second to realize that the voice came from Frank's radio. He sat up in the darkness and rubbed his eyes. His sleep had been less than comfortable. The rocks that surrounded him were oblong blocks; the smallest must have weighed half a ton. No matter which way he had attempted to lie, he had found a sharp edge digging into his body.

'Fraser, you had a good sleep?' Kirby sounded cheerful and confident. 'We're coming in after you, buddy. No use trying to hide or outrun us. It's payback time. Don't want to talk? Never mind, we'll be seeing you soon.'

He eased the stiffness from his body and winced. The bullet graze on his shoulder stung like hell and his body protested against half a dozen bad bruises and cuts. He forced himself to ignore the pain. Why had Kirby warned him he was coming? What the hell was he up to? He soon had his answer.

For the first time, he saw them before he heard them. A light suddenly filled the tunnel. He watched from his hiding place as they came into view, his breath stilled. Two men, each with his own cover, held arc lights that Kirby had rigged up. A combat team of four skirmished along the tunnel. At the perimeter of the lighted area they took cover until the lights were brought forward. When the team came upon a side tunnel, one light was diverted to search it with a second combat team of four. Fraser edged backwards into total darkness. They were going to search every tunnel in the system until they found him. Even with his night goggles, he couldn't move fast enough to stay ahead of them. If he didn't slow them up, they would catch him – and very quickly.

*

Galbraith stepped out into the early-morning sunshine and for once ignored the twitching curtains in the house opposite. As he strode up the hill he considered his conversation with Melrose. Hamilton had believed a man named Carter had disappeared on the McLeod estate. It was too much of a coincidence for it not to be the same man. The problem was: who to trust? The inquiry from the Met was a godsend: it would allow him to ask a few questions, get a few facts straight. After that – well, that all depended on how Johnstone reacted.

Angus, looking anxious, met him at the door of the police station.

'Mr Johnstone is waiting for you in your office, Chief Inspector.'

'He's early. Does he know about the phone call I had last night?'

'No, Mr Galbraith. I thought you'd like to tell him yourself.'

'Good, Angus.' Galbraith tapped his nose with a long finger. 'Let's just keep it in house for the moment, eh?'

Angus adopted a knowing look. 'Right you are, Mr Galbraith.'

'Good man. Take this,' said Galbraith, handing Angus a piece of paper. 'Check if this car has been seen anywhere in the neighbourhood in the last week or so.'

Galbraith threw open his office door. 'Sorry I wasn't here to great you personally, Superintendent, but I didn't expect you this earl. . .' The words died in Galbraith's throat. The Superintendent was not alone. Seated beside him was Edward Braxton. Johnstone was wearing his full uniform, Braxton a camel-coloured cashmere overcoat over a grey, double-breasted Armani suit.

'Come in, Chief Inspector, and close the door,' said Johnstone quietly. 'We don't want the whole station to hear our business. You've not met Mr Braxton, I believe.'

Galbraith looked at the American. 'I haven't had the pleasure.'

Braxton inclined his head slightly but did not extend his hand.

'After our talk last night I decided to make a few inquiries,' Johnstone continued. 'It seems you were right: Hamilton's death was no accident.'

Galbraith's gaze moved from one man to the other. 'Really?'

'Yes. I'm afraid it was suicide,' said Braxton.

Galbraith pulled a cigarette from his pocket and lit it. His half-closed eyes fixed on the American through a screen of smoke. 'Do you have some proof of this?'

Braxton nodded. 'He'd been appropriating cash for months. Nearly £20,000. When I found out about it and confronted him I told him I was going to report the matter to the police.'

'It was unfortunate that his wife was here at the time,' Johnstone said. 'From what she told you, it seems her fears were genuine. Perhaps she told Brian she was going to leave him.' He shrugged. 'Who knows? He must have forced her to drink, knowing what effect it would have, and then drove them both to their deaths.'

Galbraith kept his face impassive, as if considering this turn of events. 'Mr Braxton, how was it that none of your people noticed anything unusual?'

Braxton gave an apologetic shrug. 'We're running a big security operation in the north woods in preparation for when the hunting lodge opens. Some very important people will be staying up at McLeod House . . . Senators, Congressmen.'

He flashed a smile. 'Who knows? I might even get the odd president to visit. So there was only a skeleton staff in the house.'

Galbraith noticed that Braxton's smile never reached his eyes. 'I see,' he said softly.

A silence followed.

'How do you want me to write this up?' Galbraith asked at last.

'I'll leave that to your discretion. Chief Inspector,' Johnstone said, getting to his feet. 'I'll endorse any report you care to make.'

'I appreciate that, sir. And thank you both for coming to explain things to me.' Galbraith followed the two men out to the street. Braxton's car pulled up and the driver jumped out smartly to open the rear door. Johnstone got in. Braxton paused, holding out his hand.

'I'm real sorry we had to meet like this, Chief Inspector. Maybe you'd like to come up to the house some time for dinner.'

Galbraith accepted his hand. 'I'd like that.'

He watched as the car drew away. Any questions he'd had about Johnstone had been answered. 'Well, Ian,' he said softly to himself, 'you're on your own. You're going to have to be careful, very careful indeed.' He strode back into the police station.

Charlotte Reynolds watched his retreating back. She had just tried to contact her superior in London, but he had not answered. It could mean only one thing: he had been compromised and she was on her own. They had both known this might happen and accepted the risks. As far as she was aware, only one person could have tipped off the opposition.

*

Fraser waited in the darkness. Bruised and aching, he nestled behind two stalagmites. He had taken a considerable risk by scrambling through the tunnel to give himself enough distance to plan and think. Even so, time had been all too short. Angry cries boomed through the rocky confines of the subterranean world.

Light suddenly flooded into the tunnels, throwing contorted shadows over the walls. He saw them and felt a stab of fear. They were much closer than he had anticipated. He thought about squirming backwards to give himself more room, but realized he had no time. The point man was almost there.

Kirby had been rotating his forward men every hundred yards or so, keeping them fresh and alert. He didn't know how far ahead of him Fraser was, but he guessed they must be getting close by now. He stood immediately behind the left-hand arc light as his four-man team pushed forward. Ahead of him the ground rose steeply.

'Keep frosty, people. Our boy can't be too far ahead now.'

The pace had been frantic. Sweat poured in rivulets down his face, but he ignored it as he concentrated on the ground in front of him. He would let his forward men get to the two large stalagmites up ahead, hold them there until they brought up the lights, then swap the front team with the men behind him. Where the hell was Fraser? He had to be close. The point man was some way ahead when he gave a shout.

'Trip-wire. I've tripped a fucking wire.'

'Get down!' Kirby just had time to scream before an orange and red inferno engulfed them.

Fraser had his head down, his fingers in his ears and his mouth open when the grenade went off. He had stretched a length of fishing line across the tunnel and attached it to an

M1 grenade he had taken from Frank. Despite the fact that it contained only two ounces of C4 high explosive, in the confined space the eruption was awesome. Even worse was the shrapnel. Splintering off roll after roll of tightly bound steel wire, thousands of projectiles filled the air, each capable of killing or wounding.

The two leading members of the team caught the full brunt of the burst. Both were shredded. The third had been hit by over a dozen razor-sharp fragments of wire and was screaming for assistance. The fourth had been hit by a single fragment, just below the groin; it had cut open his femoral artery. He was lying still, concussed by the explosion, blood pumping in a crimson tide from his wound. He would be dead within ninety seconds.

Kirby, still dazed by the grenade's explosion, got slowly to his feet. The place looked like a charnel-house. He could see one of his men screaming but could hear nothing. He tapped his ear and gradually the shrieking pierced the dull ringing in his head. Then, at the end of the passageway, he saw a movement and found his voice. 'The bastard's there, at the top of the slope. Fire!'

Fraser had been much closer to the explosion than he intended. He knew the risks of using even a small amount of explosive in a confined space. There was no escape from the detonation wave which would rebound off the walls, increasing in power: the 'overpressure' could cut a man in two. The shrapnel had missed him, but he had felt himself being pitched violently back along the passage. With the air forced out of his lungs, he was barely conscious as he lifted his head groggily, trying to locate his enemies.

Kirby's shout dragged him back to his senses and he instinctively hugged the ground as rounds screeched off the rock face. A chunk of stalactite torn away by the force of the firing from below crashed on to him. Somehow it seemed to clear his head. He brought up his own rifle and returned fire. He aimed at the arc lights and had the satisfaction of seeing one of them explode, but before he could switch his sights to the next the fire on to his position intensified. The stalactites above him disintegrated. He had chosen his ambush position well and had only to crawl backwards a couple of yards and then roll to the right to be out of Kirby's direct line of fire. He donned his goggles and scrambled to his feet. Behind him he heard the firing become more sporadic as they skirmished towards his last position. He scurried into the welcoming darkness, knowing they would think twice about pursuing him further. The grenade must have given them a bit of a shock.

Behind him the firing stopped and he heard Kirby say, 'He's moved on. Bring up the light.'

Why was Kirby pushing on so recklessly, not even pausing to look after his wounded? It was unlike the man he had come to know. He increased his speed, trying to put more distance between himself and Kirby's remaining team. His foot turned on a boulder and he fell hard. It saved his life.

In front of him the tunnel was lit with gun flashes. He counted three, maybe four weapons. He started to crawl backwards and heard Kirby's voice again.

'Sam, that you?'

'That's right, Mr Kirby. We got him trapped between us.' The voice was triumphant and no more than twenty yards to his front.

'Good work, Sam. How d'ya like them apples, Fraser? Your time's up, buddy.'

Fraser was lying in a slight depression in the passageway

floor. He raised his head. There was a side tunnel about a yard ahead. Could he reach it? He fumbled in his top pocket for the second grenade and pulled the pin.

'Here's what I think, Kirby. GRENADE!' He screamed the last word and threw the M1 towards Weaver. Instinctively, Kirby and his men stepped behind the cover offered by the bend.

'Oh shit!' shouted Weaver, before rolling backwards and scrambling out of the way.

Fraser bounded to his feet and ran for the side tunnel. The M1 was designed as a defensive grenade, to be thrown by troops in trenches at oncoming infantry. It had a delay of only three seconds after the lever was released. Fraser had been on his feet almost as soon as he had thrown the device, but even so he had no sooner flung himself into the side tunnel than he heard it explode. The detonation wave threw him flat on his face. He got unsteadily to his feet and staggered along the narrow passage. After about ten feet it widened on his left-hand side and he stepped round a sharp corner, even as he heard the sounds of pursuit.

Looking back along the short corridor, he saw a dark shape blur against the tunnel entrance. He whipped up his MP5 and fired a short, three-round burst, knowing instinctively that he had missed. His knees suddenly felt weak, and he allowed himself to slide down the rock wall until he was seated with his back against it. Shoving the MP5 round the corner, he loosed off another short burst to deter any thoughts of an immediate assault, then threw back his head, eyes closed, and drew in long, shuddering breaths.

Weaver, the first man to the side tunnel entrance, had narrowly missed being caught by his first burst of fire and stood with his back against the wall as Kirby arrived.

'He made it into a side tunnel, Mr . . .'

Fraser's second burst interrupted him, making further explanation unnecessary.

'I'll get the rest of the boys and the lights. We'll . . .' Kirby told him.

Weaver gripped his boss's arm. 'Mr Kirby, I know this side tunnel. I recced it myself. It's a dead end.'

Kirby's eyes gleamed in the darkness. 'You sure?'

'Positive.'

Kirby turned to the man standing behind him and said, 'Get back to the holding area and bring me back two C4 demolition packs.' As the man nodded and sped into the darkness, Kirby grinned at Weaver.

Fraser sat in the darkness listening to the sounds from the other end of the side tunnel. He chanced a glimpse round the corner. There were lights and shadows but no movement towards him.

He considered his situation. It would be madness for his pursuers to rush up the narrow corridor towards him, but in turn he couldn't move from his present position, not even to make a preliminary exploration of this side tunnel. The confined entrance opened out into a high cavern and even with the aid of his goggles he couldn't make out the far walls.

He looked at his watch, then checked it again. To his shock, it was not yet noon. It was going to be a long day. He had just made up his mind to move when heard a muffled shout.

'Fire in the hold.'

The explosion was thunderous and he was thrown across the cavern, to land with a thud against the wall. His brain had time to register a blinding, red-hot pain, then a deep, warm, familiar darkness.

He heard his name called from across a ballroom and saw

Lindsey, draped in shimmering black satin, glide across the floor towards him. He took her cool hand lightly and they were dancing ever faster as the tempo increased, twirling, dizzily, their reflections smiling back at them from the heavy gilt mirrors lining the walls. He bent to kiss her, but as he did so the ballroom was transformed into a forest and Lindsey cried out in fright.

He looked around and saw Kirby conducting the orchestra, only they had AK47s instead of violins and the music was a wave of gunfire as Lindsey's face dissolved in a red mist.

He came to with a start. His watch had been smashed during the explosion. For how long he had blacked out he had no idea. He sat up and moved his head gently. He knew that to move too soon would result in nausea, even unconsciousness.

He sat motionless for several minutes, then clambered unsteadily to his feet and switched on his torch. The entrance tunnel had been obliterated by the collapse of the roof: huge lumps of stone had crashed to the ground inches from where he had been sitting. He whistled softly.

'It doesn't get much closer than that, Fraser, my boy.'

He swung the torch beam around and located his night goggles, which he slipped on, giving thanks that they still worked. However, he still could not make out the ceiling of the cavern but after moving less than twenty feet he found the wall. Keeping one hand touching it, he edged along, stepping over and around the rocks that the explosion had scattered across the floor of the cave.

Half an hour later he found himself back where he had started, at the collapsed entrance tunnel. He repeated the process, this time searching thoroughly for an exit route, however small. There was none. He ripped off the goggles and flashed his torch over the ceiling. There was a squeal of alarm as he disturbed a colony of bats. The creatures flew in irregular patterns to escape his torch beam as he sought any sign of an opening.

Nothing. He was entombed, and trying to come to terms with the fact, when his radio crackled.

'Fraser, can you hear me?' It was Kirby again. 'If you're still alive, by now you'll have realized there's no way out.'

Fraser fought the impulse to scream his rage.

'I'd have preferred to finish you man to man, but . . .' – Fraser could imagine the man's nonchalant shrug – 'this'll have to do.'

Fraser swung his torch in a tight circle, his face set in grim defiance, then switched it off to preserve its power.

'I'll say goodbye now, Fraser,' said the American. His voice was flat, unemotional. 'I'd like to say it's been fun, but it hasn't.'

The radio died.

13

Galbraith stared out of his office window. Clouds hung low over Bannock and shrouded the surrounding hills. The afternoon was heavy and grey. Rain had threatened all day but never materialized, so, despite the early hour, he had the heating turned up and the lights on. The weather depressed him.

He had sat for most of the day deep in contemplation of the pile of official papers in front of him, untouched except for a dusting of ash. A knock on his door interrupted his deliberations. Angus's face appeared. 'Do you have a moment, Chief Inspector? It's about that car.'

'Someone's spotted it?'

'Well, yes and no.'

Galbraith hid his exasperation, knowing the desk sergeant would tell the story in his own way, however long it took.

'The way it is, four nights ago, Finlay MacDonald had a skinful at the Marquis and he and Dougie Thompson got into a frightful argument about the time Dougie's father ran for office for the district council against Finlay and how Finlay always claimed he bought votes by offering free drinks. Sure they're always arguing about it if you ask me . . .'

'The car, Angus,' Galbraith reminded him gently.

'Oh aye. Anyway, Dougie threw Finlay out again, and called PC Lang because Finlay started to urinate against the cars in the car park.'

'And PC Lang cautioned him.'

'Aye, that's right, but Lang has always had a thing about cars and he remembered that one of the cars was' – Angus looked at his note book – 'a black Jaguar XJ6.'

'Did he get the registration number?' Galbraith asked, knowing the answer.

'No, sir, he did not.'

Galbraith sighed.

'But he did speak to the driver, a Mr Carter. Didn't get his first name. An Englishman, said he was in a hurry and didn't want any further action.'

Galbraith let out a low whistle of satisfaction. 'Do you think PC Lang would recognize the man again?'

Angus shook his head sadly. 'First thing I asked him, sir. No chance, I'm afraid. It was dark in the car park. All he can say is that the man was English, medium build, about five foot nine, well spoken and well dressed.'

'I'll need a statement from PC Lang, a detailed statement, everything he can remember. Then I want you to go down to the Marquis, ask Finlay and Dougie if they remember the man. If they don't, find out who else was in the bar that night and see if you can rustle up anybody who spoke to the man or remembers him. Keep this to yourself, Angus – I don't want it all round the station.'

'Right you are, Mr Galbraith.' Then Angus remembered the sheet of paper in his hand. 'There is this too, sir,' he said.

Galbraith, his mind absorbed by the new information, accepted it without glancing at it. He hardly noticed as Angus left. It wasn't enough – even with Anne's letter it wasn't enough – to go to a higher authority and accuse his own boss of corruption. That was what he faced, corruption. What was worse he had no idea how far it went and whom he could trust.

Of one thing he was sure: they weren't going to get away with it, not with killing Anne. Anger started to well up inside him again. He fought against it, knowing he had to keep a cool head. He lit a cigarette. 'I'll get them for you, Anne, don't you worry about that. I'll get them.'

He glanced half-heartedly at the fax Angus had brought him. Then he read it from the start.

To all Highlands Police Stations
MISSING SERVICEMAN
Staff Sergeant Mark Fraser and his wife Lindsey have been reported missing in this area by the Ministry of Defence. Their car was found at a hotel in Inverness and the couple are believed to be on a walking holiday in the hills but are two days overdue. Staff Sergeant Fraser is required for urgent duties with his regiment. Any sightings are to be reported immediately to the nearest army base.

Galbraith threw the note into his IN tray; he had more important things to worry about than some squaddie who couldn't be bothered to report back to his unit.

Fraser had long since stopped pacing round his prison. He had gone over every inch of the walls: there wasn't even a crack. He had explored the entrance tunnel, and decided there was a way out – if he had a week, a bulldozer and ten men with picks, shovels and shoring materials.

He sat down and lit a candle from his survival pack. The

sudden light caused a squeak of alarm from the bats above him which made him look up. The walls were sheer, but there were hand holds. He turned on his torch and scanned it again for openings. There were none. So this is how it ends. He realized he had lived with the anticipation of an early death for so long it held few terrors for him.

If Lindsey had still been alive, he told himself, it would have been different. The first time he saw her he knew that she was the one, the only one, for him. They had been married within a year. She had been his best friend. When he had come back from the Gulf crippled and half mad from Iraqi torture, she had nursed him back to health and sanity. This holiday had been her idea. 'I want to see Scotland, your country, those hills you always keep bragging about.' It had been the best of times.

He breathed in the sharp, clean air, feeling it bite into his lungs. In front of him, Lindsey turned. The pale sunlight caught her upturned face, half hidden by her shoulder-length, auburn hair. A faint smile played on her lips, mischief danced in the deep azure blue of her eyes.

Fraser felt as if his heart had been seized. He stopped in his tracks. She was hauntingly beautiful. The look on his face must have disconcerted her, for her smile was replaced by a look of concern.

'Something wrong?' she said.

Instead of answering, he walked quickly towards her, slipped his arm round her waist and drew her swiftly to him. He brushed the hair from the side of her face and bent to study her for a moment before kissing her, feeling the warmth of her lips, the dart of her tongue as it teased his. Her hands entwined around the back of his neck as the kiss became more urgent.

They slipped off their packs in the early-morning mist and fell to the yielding forest floor. His hands were made suddenly awkward by their urgency. He felt her strain against him, whispering half-heard words of tenderness. Then they were oblivious to everything but each other. Afterwards they lay enfolded together, staring up through the trees

'If I was to die now, I would be a very, very happy man,' he said eventually.

She snuggled even closer. 'It's starting to rain. If we don't move soon we both will – of exposure.'

He gave her nose a light peck. 'Or exhaustion.'

'What a way to go,' she murmured, and began to nibble his ear.

He laughed and sat up. 'Wanton woman.' He looked down at her, sprawled on the soft, mossy bank. 'I don't understand what someone as lovely as you could've ever seen in somebody like me.'

Her face took on a puzzled frown and her fingers traced the contours of his face. As she touched his lips, he turned his head to kiss her palm.

'Because,' she said, her voice still barely a whisper, 'you're the kindest and warmest man I've ever met.' She paused. 'I feel safe with you.'

After about half an hour's easy walking they heard the sound of water gushing over rocks and stopped in a clearing. Fraser pulled out his map and opened it. He felt a pressure on his right arm and looked sideways at her. Lindsey was studying the map intently. He suppressed a smile, knowing the contour lines were like hieroglyphics to her.

'By my reckoning we're about a mile and a half from the A534, which leads into Bannock. We should be able to grab a bus there to Inverness.'

'I don't want to go. I could stay in these wonderful hills for ever.'

'I've got to be back by mid-afternoon tomorrow or the OC will have my guts for garters.'

'And then you'll be away again, God alone knows where or for how long.'

He was behind her now, looking at the map, hardly listening to what she said. 'I'll only be gone four months, five at the most. We can have another walking holiday when I get back, if you like.'

'It won't be the same.'

She turned from him, a quiver in her voice. He dropped the map and, putting his arms around her, pulled her gently to him. 'Of course it will be. I promised you: we'll always be together.' He felt her body tense and nuzzled her neck. 'What's wrong?'

'I won't be able to climb mountains by the time you come home.'

It took a second for the implication of her words to register, then he spun her round. 'You mean . . .?'

She nodded, her whole body taut with uncertainty and anticipation.

'How? I mean, when . . . when did you know?' The words tumbled out of his mouth.

'I found out just before we left.'

'Should you be out here? Shouldn't you be resting?'

'Don't be silly,' she said gently. 'Exercise is just what I need at this stage of pregnancy. How do you feel about it?'

'Exercise, I'm all for it.'

She punched him hard in the shoulder. 'Beast. The baby, how do you feel about it? I know we didn't plan for this.'

The joy he felt showed in his face, for her smile quickly

returned as he pulled her to him once more. 'I couldn't be happier. I hope it's a girl, just as beautiful as her mother.'

'I hope it's a boy,' Lindsey said.

'Perhaps it will be one of each.'

She pushed herself away from him. 'Don't get carried away, Fraser.'

Laughing, he threw off his pack. 'You make camp and set up the fire. I'll go get us some water and we'll have a last meal and discuss names before we get back to civilization.'

'Aye, aye, sir.' She threw a mock salute.

'That's the Navy way, foolish woman.' He smiled and ducked the lump of wood she tossed at him.

Chuckling to himself, he turned and walked the fifty or so yards to the stream. There he paused at the water's edge to look at the distant mountains, majestic among their wreaths of clouds. He bent on one knee to fill his water bottles, long practice making him keep his head up and his eyes searching the opposite banks. He had filled one bottle and was reaching for the second, when he heard gunshots. He was on his feet immediately, for it was an automatic pistol and not a hunter's weapon. Holding on to the sound, his mind was like a computer, calculating calibre, direction of fire, distance from his present position. Then he heard Lindsey: a single, heart-wrenching scream.

Before the water bottle hit the stream, he was sprinting up the steep bank towards the sound of her cry. He headed at top speed in the direction of their makeshift camp. Bursting into a clearing, he almost fell over a man's body. A swift glance told him that the man was dead. A rustling to his left made him turn sharply, just in time to catch a glimpse of a second man hurrying away. Then he heard Lindsey scream his name again.

She was close, somewhere to his left. He started to run again, frantically searching the undergrowth. Then he saw her.

She was running headlong towards the stream, her arms outstretched. He drew in a deep gulp of air to shout to her as the shattering bark of the automatic came again — four shots in quick succession — and as in a slow-motion nightmare he saw her hit, saw the crimson stain spreading over her breast. She rose on tiptoe, staggered a few more feet, then collapsed.

Years of training forced him to search for the source of the gunfire. A broad-shouldered man emerged from the trees to his left holding a heavy automatic pistol. He was close enough to identify the weapon: it was an Israeli-made Desert Eagle .357 magnum automatic. He covered the distance between them in seconds.

His quarry was concentrating on the woman, unsure whether he had killed or merely wounded her. Then the huge man heard a noise to his right. He looked towards his charging adversary and saw his own death approaching.

Fraser grabbed the man's outstretched right arm with his left hand, his fingers biting into his tendons like steel claws. His right hand came up, fingers outstretched. The edge of his hand chopped his opponent's wrist with a sickening crack and the pistol dropped from nerveless fingers. Before the man could even scream, Fraser smashed his elbow into his nose, just below the bridge, squashing it flat against his face.

The massive blow drove the man backwards and before he could begin to fight back Fraser was on him. Three short jabs, two to the face and one to the solar plexus, robbed him of the power to breathe. Moving as if he was underwater, he threw an ineffectual right hook.

Fraser stepped inside it and drove his right elbow hard against the man's head. The force of the blow spun him around. Fraser took a half step to his right and stamped down with his heavily booted foot, catching his adversary behind his knee. The leg collapsed, throwing the man on to his knees. Fraser brought up his right foot, pushing rather than kicking him, down on to his face.

Kneeling on the man's broad back, he seized his chin with a cupped hand and applied pressure with the other. He took a deep breath, focused his strength and twisted violently. There was a sound like a rotten branch cracking.

Fraser rushed towards Lindsey. The damage to her back was too awful to look at. As he gently turned her over an anguished cry escaped his lips. Her face was still beautiful, despite the creeping greyness of death. He pulled her shredded jacket tight to shield the ruin that had been her chest and rocked backwards and forwards, sobbing softly.

He was unable to say for sure how long he had been sitting there – time meant nothing to him – when he heard a noise. His head came up. Three men were standing by the body of the man he had killed. He recognized the one he had seen hurrying away from the clearing. Their eyes locked. The man pointed a meaty finger at him.

'Get that sonofabitch.'

One of his companions unslung a rifle.

Fraser rolled sideways, keeping flat until he was in the nearest cover, then, rising like a sprinter, took off at speed for the stream. Above his head he heard the crack of a bullet and behind him the noise of the men's close pursuit. He swerved sharply to the right, hit the bank and half ran, half slid down it. His feet hit the water and it suddenly erupted as more bullets slammed into its surface. He risked a quick look over his shoulder and saw two men in the act of re-cocking bolt-action rifles. They were less than twenty yards behind him. He took off along the stream's edge, heading for the high ground in the distance, praying he could lose them in the rough country ahead.

*

Fraser looked into the candle's flickering light. He knew now that the bodies of those men were lying next to Lindsey's, where none could mourn them. And now he would share their grave. 'So that's it then with only a few bats for company.' He looked up as he mumbled to himself, his eyes narrowing as he focused on the vaulted ceiling of his future tomb. Then he sprang to his feet, grabbed a torch and probed the top of the cave with its beam. The place was empty. The bats had disappeared.

Kirby placed the Kurtz sub-machine-gun on the refectory table in McLeod House. Around him his men settled wearily into chairs. Slumping down heavily himself, the security chief picked up the gun and removed its double thirty-round magazine, then cocked it to remove the round in the chamber, before pointing the weapon at the floor and pulling the trigger. He heard the soft click as the hammer fell. The rest of the security team followed his example.

A dreadful tiredness suddenly threatened to over-whelm him and he dropped his head into his hands, feeling wearier than he could remember. He rubbed the heels of his hands into his eyes, then groped in his pocket for a cigar. When he looked up Braxton was framed in the door-way.

'Is it over?' the tycoon asked.

Kirby lit his cigar before answering.

'Yeah, it's over. He's dead, or soon will be.'

'What do you mean, "or soon will be"?'

Irritated, Kirby looked away. 'We've sealed him up in one of the side chambers. If the blast didn't kill him, starvation will.' Briefly he outlined the final confrontation.

'You're sure there was no way out?'

Kirby shook his head. 'Sam's been over every inch of those tunnels. He says it's a dead end.'

Weaver smiled. 'That's right, Mr Braxton. It's a dead end all right. A fly couldn't get out of that side tunnel.'

Braxton felt relief flood over him. He remembered Fraser's expression when he held his dead wife in his arms.

'Good, good. There's a $10,000 bonus for each of you in this.'

Silence greeted his offer.

'Where are the rest of your crew?'

Kirby glanced around at the strained faces of his men. 'This is it, apart from a skeleton guard at the front gate and the potholes.'

'Jesus,' Braxton muttered.

'I lost another seven men dead and one badly injured. Somehow he got hold of some grenades, probably off Frank – the damn fool loved bangs. In that confined space they were lethal.' Kirby shook his head. 'I left the dead in there. We'll seal them in with the containers. Can I have your permission to call in a medevac chopper. We need to fly the wounded over to the French hospital.'

Braxton nodded, still numb.

'As for the rest of you boys,' Kirby went on, raising his voice slightly. 'Clean your weapons and stack your gear, then stand down for thirty-six hours. Sam, organize a minimal team to look after the front gate and the potholes. Anybody who wants to can go into Bannock. Parade in this hall 0800 hours, day after tomorrow.'

The men got to their feet slowly and filed out with hardly a word. Only Braxton, Kirby and Weaver remained.

Braxton broke the silence. 'Do you have enough men to cover the operation?'

'Just about. But once it's over we'll have to recruit more and that'll take time. The kind of guys we need aren't that easy to find.'

'Anything you want, just ask,' Braxton said. 'Sir Marcus came through. He managed to muzzle the Carter investigation.'

Kirby rubbed his eyes, too tired to answer.

'He also found the source of the SIS investigation. He won't be giving us any more trouble either.'

'What about Charlotte Reynolds?' Kirby asked.

Braxton smiled for the first time. 'She's not a problem. Sir Marcus believes she may be with the SIS and he has identified her controller. She'll be taken care of. Without headquarters back-up, she can't get anywhere. She has nobody to report to, nobody to protect her.'

Kirby got to his feet. 'Then she'll be as glad to get the hell out of this God-forsaken hole as I will.' He looked at Weaver. 'At least it's not like Somalia, Sam.'

'How do you mean, Mr Kirby?'

'I don't have to write to the families. I always hated that.' Without waiting for an answer, he turned and left.

Fraser had spent an age studying the cave with his torch. He could make out a ledge, just below the ceiling. It was at least thirty-five feet, and the rock-face from which it projected was vertical. With adequate climbing equipment it would be a difficult climb; without, a bloody nightmare. He picked out a route that offered some chance of success and stripped to his shirt to begin the climb, leaving everything but his torch and pistol on the ground.

In the heady early days of his army career he had broken one of the professional soldier's great unwritten laws: never volunteer. He had offered to undertake the Belgian Para-

Commandos' rock-climbing course. Three weeks of terrifying, body-bruising hell, supervised by experts who climbed like their hands and feet were covered with Superglue. He searched back in his memory for guidance. 'Choose your route in advance, keep three points of contact at all times.' He reflected that at least then he had been climbing in daylight. But just looking at it wasn't going to make it any easier. He started upwards.

After the first few feet the wall became like black glass. His hand and toe holds were little more than slight indentations, none more than a fraction of an inch wide, in the rock. He felt a slight crack and jammed his knife in up to the hilt, tested it by pulling down sharply, then levered himself up another few feet.

Looking up, he could make out the ledge, still a good ten feet above him. His hands searched for a hold, crack or fissure, but found none. Then he noticed a small lump of rock jutting out about half a foot beyond his reach. If he could just grasp that the ledge would be accessible. He was standing on one foot, supported by his wedged knife. Could he jump the six inches or so to reach the protrusion? Would it support him? If not then it was a sliding fall of twenty feet or so to the bottom of the rock-face. He took a deep breath, gathered all his strength, bent one leg as far as he dared and pushed away.

Both hands reached the rock. His left fell away immediately, unable to gain a hold on the wet surface, but his right found just enough purchase to keep a hold. For a moment his body swung in mid-air, supported by the strength of four fingers, then he swung the other hand upwards and felt another hand hold. With a grunt he heaved as his feet scrambled to find a grip, and he levered himself upwards.

Seconds later he found a foothold and reached for the ledge just above him.

The ledge was larger than Fraser had expected: at least ten feet long and three deep. He sat for a second, his back to the wall, his feet dangling into space, drawing deep gulps of air. When his breathing returned to normal he looked round and his heart sank. The wall behind him looked solid. He switched on his torch and saw more clearly that to his right, where the back wall met the ledge, there was a small opening. He crawled towards it.

It was barely twenty inches in diameter. Ducking his head, he looked along its length. It sloped upwards and, if anything, got slightly smaller along its winding length. But it gave him hope. He kept the torch in his hand and stuck his pistol inside his boot. He would need every inch of space around his waist. As he was about to crawl inside he thought, some people do this for fun, but if I get out of here I'm going to live on Salisbury Plain, where there's open space and no bloody caves.

Galbraith eyed the clock on his office wall. Just after seven and already it was dusk. He had been out all day trying to trace the movements of Carter's Jaguar. There was one possible sighting about three days ago. During the early hours of the morning a local farmer tending a sick cow saw a similar car heading towards Inverness at speed.

His phone rang. 'Chief Inspector Galbraith. Superintendent Melrose.'

Galbraith knew something was wrong. He waited for the other man to continue.

'Carter's death is now officially listed as a burglary that went wrong and I have been reassigned to other work.'

Galbraith could hear the bitterness in the man's voice.

'I'm sorry,' he said, realizing how inadequate it sounded.

'Not your fault, old son. Any news for me?'

'Not much. The car's been seen but it's hardly enough to turn things around.' He dared not mention Anne's letter.

The Englishman laughed. 'I'd need an open-and-shut case to make anyone listen at the moment. There seems to be some pretty heavy pressure being applied upstairs.'

That had a familiar ring to it. 'I'll keep digging at this end,' Galbraith promised.

'Good, I'd appreciate that. If you get anything ring me at home, day or night.' He recited the number. 'And thanks again, Chief Inspector.'

Galbraith replaced the receiver and made his way out of the station, too wrapped up in his own thoughts to hear the desk sergeant's goodnight. He dawdled home, oblivious to the light rain that had started to fall. He walked into his front room. His personal papers were scattered everywhere. He let out a brief exclamation and then stood very still. He always did when he was looking down the barrel of a Smith and Wesson .45 automatic held in perfectly steady hands.

14

Galbraith was mesmerized by Charlotte's automatic, its black muzzle centred on his head.

It was she who broke the silence. 'When's Operation Hades set to begin?'

Galbraith's confusion deepened. 'What the hell's Operation Hades?'

'Don't take me for a fool. I know you're working for Braxton. He told you who I was.'

'Braxton has never told me anything.'

'Then how did you know that first day we met that I was with the Intelligence Service?'

'Whoever trained you didn't have enough time. I spent five years in Special Branch and worked with SIS agents all the time. When you first walked into my office the jacket you were wearing was tailored to cover a shoulder holster and when you're not carrying a gun the left lapel always drops noticeably. Then the calluses on your hand show you've undergone both weapon training and unarmed combat. To anyone who could spot the signs it's as if you had a sign hanging round your neck saying "Charlotte Reynolds SIS".'

She nodded imperceptibly. 'So who primed Kirby?'

'I told Braxton nothing. If anyone tipped him off about

you, it was Superintendent Johnstone. Braxton's bought him body and soul.'

'I'm supposed to believe that?' Charlotte's voice had risen a fraction.

His frustration beginning to surface, Galbraith growled, 'I really don't give a damn what you believe,' then slipped his hand inside his jacket.

'Careful,' Charlotte warned him.

Galbraith pulled back his jacket to reveal Anne's letter in the inside pocket. 'Read this, then either put down the gun and tell me what this is all about, or use it.'

Charlotte continued to eye him uncertainly while she scanned the letter. 'I'm sorry,' she said, abruptly dropping her gun hand and relaxing her posture. Suddenly she appeared very vulnerable. 'My control has cut contact.'

Galbraith indicated a chair. 'Sit down, Miss Reynolds, and I'll get us both a tea. I don't know about you, but I could do with one.'

Over a steaming mug of sweet tea, Charlotte explained that she was a physics graduate and had been recruited into the Secret Intelligence Service only six weeks ago. Her control was a long-time friend of her family and a senior member of the SIS. There was no one else in the department he could trust.

'Braxton has either bribed, intimidated or blackmailed key SIS members and senior civil servants.'

'What exactly were you supposed to do?'

'I was to meet a man called Carter who had something on Braxton. Just question him, assess his information and get it back to London. But now my contact's lost and I'm completely out of my depth.'

'That must be the same man Anne mentions in her letter – the Customs man.'

'How do you know he worked for Customs?'

'I was contacted by the Met . . . a Superintendent Melrose. He knew there was something odd about Carter's death. The body was found in his flat but he wasn't killed there. He had extended hypostasis to both chest and back.' Galbraith noticed the puzzled look on the young woman's face. 'After death the blood pools on whichever side the body is lying. It shows up during the post-mortem as a bright-red stain. Carter's body was stained both front and back, which means that it lay for some time in one position after he was dead and was later turned over.'

'I see.'

'Now it's your turn. What in hell's name is this all about? What information were you expecting Carter to pass you?'

Charlotte paused to collect her thoughts. 'You know that Braxton has signed a deal to reprocess spent fuel rods at Dunston?'

Galbraith nodded.

'During the procedure ninety-six per cent of the spent fuel rods are reprocessed into reusable uranium. Although the US atomic industry has been in private ownership since the Three Mile Island disaster they've been unable to undertake any reprocessing work. But, for our sins, we lead the world in the field and that's why they ship their waste over here. Only this time we think Braxton slipped something extra into his last shipment.'

'What?'

'How much do you know about nuclear waste?'

An hour later he knew a great deal. His face was ashen as he looked at Charlotte and said, 'It isn't possible – nobody could be that stupid.'

'It is possible, and it's not that stupid – at least not

from Braxton's perspective. The American Atomic Energy Commission has draconian powers. Even a minor transgression can result in almost unlimited fines and confiscation of assets. All he needs is somewhere isolated to dump the stuff.'

'But what about the damage to the environment?'

She shrugged. 'He won't be around to see it. What's our next step?'

Galbraith rubbed a hand over his eyes. 'With Johnstone in their pocket we don't have enough to get an inquiry off the ground. And with Hamilton and Anne dead, her letter is worthless as evidence in a court of law.'

'I have a back-up, a direct line to a ministerial contact. He's hard-headed but as straight as a die. If I can get proof to him he'll get an inquiry started. There's only one place I can get that proof.'

Galbraith thought it over for several seconds. 'We don't have much choice, do we?' he said.

Charlotte shook her head. 'I've got to get on to Braxton's estate.'

Galbraith smiled wearily. 'I can usually find some excuse to get myself invited in.' He clicked his fingers and his smile became more genuine. 'We had a message in today about a missing soldier and his wife: perfect. What else do you need?'

Charlotte grabbed a pen and piece of paper from Galbraith's desk and started to compile a list.

Fraser felt as if he was being squeezed to death. Twice his shoulders were stuck fast between the rock walls and he could only move forward by expelling all the air from his lungs. Progress was now measured in inches. Worse still, the torch was dimming. He switched it off.

Something brushed against his face in the darkness: something furry. He tried to bring his right arm back to brush whatever it was away and only succeeded in scraping his knuckles against the rock. There was a swish of cold air across his face and he let out an involuntary yell and flashed the torch. The bat squeaked and flew away from him. He sighed and rested his head on his outstretched arm. The cold was becoming a problem. His thin shirt was soaking wet, and he shivered uncontrollably, his teeth chattering like castanets as his body fought to retain heat. He longed to be able to rub some life and warmth into his aching limbs.

He forced himself not to think about the cold or the pain, to concentrate instead on easing himself forward. He had no idea how far he'd come since squeezing into the narrow fissure. Now he had to rest frequently. He didn't know which was worse: the excruciating pain of movement or the numbing cold when he rested.

He started forward again and his outstretched right hand found only space. He switched on the torch once more. In its feeble light he saw he had come to a sudden vertical drop. He inched forward and peered over the edge, but could see nothing in the wavering beam. Directly in front of him was a solid wall of rock. He shone the torch upwards and let out a sigh of relief. There was another tunnel to his right, about three feet higher, on the opposite wall. He judged the gap to be about six feet. Not too far to jump if you were fresh, had a running start and weren't doing it in total darkness.

On his side of the drop there was a slight, tapering ledge which ran along the rock-face until it was almost directly across from the other tunnel. He turned on to his back and grasped the low roof, then used his legs to lever himself upright. Pins and needles racked his newly liberated limbs and when he thought he could trust his legs to support him he swung his body around until his back was against the wall. The ledge was barely wide enough for him to balance. He aimed the torch across the roof of the cavern, from which long straw stalactites hung down. As the beam touched them it unleashed a shower of brilliant light. For a moment Fraser understood why potholers risked their lives in these cold, dangerous depths. It was breathtakingly beautiful.

He blew noisily through his chattering teeth. If he lost his footing there was nothing to stop his fall for at least a hundred feet, maybe more. He switched off the torch, put his head back against the wall and began to make his way very slowly along the ledge, pressing his back against the damp, icy rock. His right heel dislodged a loose stone and threw his leg into space. He fought to counter the sudden loss of balance and control his panic. When he had regained his foothold he stood, glued to the wall, his heart pounding. He listened as the stone tumbled downwards, bouncing off the cavern wall. The sound was lost to him long before it reached the bottom.

After three more minutes of shuffling he judged that he was opposite the tunnel, and switched on his torch. It was directly across the abyss, almost level with his head. As part of the brutal P Company selection process he had had to jump from one platform to another across a six-foot space, suspended forty feet in the air. But he had been seventeen then, a young Parachute Regiment recruit. Now he was tired, wet, hungry and suffering from half a dozen injuries of varying severity.

If his experience had taught him anything it was that if you had a dangerous thing to do it was best to do it quickly. There was no way he could jump while holding the torch. He would need both hands to grasp the ledge – if he reached it. Never once taking his eyes off his target, he switched off the torch and stowed it in his pocket. Gathering himself, he bent his knees as far as he dared, feeling his back slide down the wall. He stretched out his arms, pumped the muscles in his thighs and leapt into mid-air.

As soon as he left the rock-face it felt as if his heart and lungs were being pulled into the pit of his stomach. He was dropping straight down in an endless, timeless fall. In his mind's eye he saw the vast space open up below him. He gritted his teeth, and moved his legs wildly to gain momentum. His hands stretched out for the ledge he knew was there but which seemed so far beyond reach. His mouth opened wide to scream a last word of defiance. The rock wall hit him with the force of a Tyson right cross. His elbows took the brunt of the impact, the pain seared his arms. Even as his body registered the shock, his hands scrambled for a grip, fingernails scraping against rock in desperation as his body weight dragged him backwards. Inch by inch he was sliding back into oblivion.

He splayed both hands wide and shouted with blessed relief as they found a hold: a deep crack in the ledge on one side, an upthrust rock on the other. His backward slide stopped and he scrabbled frantically with his feet, fear lending him added strength. Gradually he levered himself up until he could throw an elbow and forearm on to the ledge. He paused, taking the time for one deep breath to centre what remained of his strength, then pulled his body up and over.

He rolled on to the ledge and gulped air into his lungs. Pain surged through his body. From the torn fingernails, to the savagely lacerated elbows and knees, every bit of his body was on fire. But he was alive.

As his breath came back a fit of uncontrollable laughter racked him, torturing his straining lungs. A joke he had heard a long time ago, a squeaking voice repeating the same line over and over again. The laughter convulsed him. He threw his head back and roared out the punch-line:

'I'm not dead yet!'

Galbraith was surprised at the uncharacteristic lapse in inefficiency. It took the gate guard ten minutes to respond to his persistent ringing. The imposing iron gates of McLeod House swung slowly open, squealing in protest on their electronically powered hinges. A tall, lean American in his late twenties approached the Chief Inspector and flashed a torch into the Land Rover.

Galbraith put a hand in front of his eyes. 'All right, laddie. Can't you see I'm on my own and this is a police vehicle?' His voice was gruff and authoritative. The sentry almost came to attention.

'Sorry, sir. We weren't expecting any visitors at this time.'

'Aye, well, this is an emergency. Would you inform either Mr Braxton or Mr Kirby that I need to speak to them immediately?'

'Yessir.'

The sentry walked quickly to the nearby gatehouse, a small concrete and glass monstrosity that looked out of place beside the hand-wrought gates. Galbraith heard the squelch of an intercom and a voice raised in anger. The sentry threw him a worried look and spoke softly into the microphone.

Galbraith held his breath. If Kirby came down to the front gate his plan would be in ruins. He affected nonchalance, but watched the sentry intently out of the corner of his eye. He saw the young man nod twice and seconds later he was back beside the Land Rover's window. Galbraith turned his head slowly and looked up.

'Mr Braxton and Mr Kirby will meet you at the house.'

'Thank you, laddie, I know the way.' Throwing the Land Rover into first, he took off up the drive. When the sentry was no longer in his rear-view mirror he stopped abruptly. Charlotte rolled out of the rear seat and kept low, edging up until she was by his window.

'Keep that listening watch,' she whispered. 'I'll be in touch.'

By the time Galbraith turned his head the trees had engulfed her.

Braxton and Kirby were on the front steps, flanking Superintendent Johnstone, whose face was rigid with anger. 'What do you mean, bothering Mr Braxton at this time of night? You'd better have an extremely good reason.'

'I do, sir.' Galbraith enjoyed his superior's discomfort. He looked up at Braxton standing in the doorway, a glass in one hand and a cigar in the other. All three men were wearing dinner jackets. 'We have a missing soldier and his wife, lost and overdue with his unit,' he said to none of them in particular. 'The MoD is hitting the roof. Apparently he has specialized knowledge and is needed immediately by his unit.'

'Which unit?' Kirby said a little too quickly.

'I don't know,' Galbraith answered. But the question puzzled him and his gaze flicked between Braxton and Kirby. What had started as a simple ruse to get Charlotte into the estate had developed into something more interesting. He carried on probing.

'I remembered the Superintendent saying something about possible trespassers in your northern woods a few days ago and wondered if any of your security patrols had seen anyone.'

'No, nothing.' Braxton's eyes narrowed.

'Really?' Galbraith fixed him with an unflinching stare. 'They must have seen something. Mr Kirby mentioned it to

Superintendent Johnstone just the other day. Isn't that right, sir?'

He turned to Johnstone, enjoying the man's confusion. 'Well, yes, Mr Kirby did mention . . .'

'My men did spot something, about three days ago. Could have been your two missing walkers.'

Galbraith saw something flicker across Braxton's face. Disbelief, anxiety? He concentrated again on Kirby, who told him, 'We searched the woods but found nothing. Then last night one of our patrols spotted two figures climbing up on the Melville Hills – could be your two lost sheep.'

Galbraith nodded slowly, his smile wide. 'That must be it. It was a long shot anyway. Please ask your men to keep a lookout and report any other sightings. I'll be heading back. Goodnight, gentlemen. Goodnight, sir.'

As Galbraith drove off, Braxton walked slowly down the steps to stand beside Kirby. Both men watched the Land Rover's disappearing tail lights.

'What do you make of that?'

'I don't know, I really don't know,' Kirby replied. 'But I think it's trouble.' He raced back into the house without waiting for a response.

Galbraith drew up at the main gates, sat for a full three minutes, then blew his horn. The noise drifted eerily through the trees. He waited a while before sounding it again. Nothing. The woods closed in around him. He turned off the engine and went to the gatehouse. It was locked and deserted. He took a deep breath and bellowed, 'Hello. Can somebody let me out?'

There was no reply, but the sound of his voice disturbed something in the bushes near by. Galbraith felt his heart pound as whatever it was scampered away. Probably a brass monkey looking for a welder. He felt the cold touch of the night air seeping through his thin working suit. He banged his hands together, blew into them as he looked around, then let out another shout.

'What do you have to do to get out of this place?'

He walked purposefully to the iron gates and gave them a violent pull. They were immovable. He let out a breath of exasperation which turned into a cry of surprise. The young sentry was standing only a foot behind him, his eyes steady and unblinking.

'Christ! You scared the living daylights out of me.'

'Sorry, sir,' the sentry muttered. 'I had to answer nature's call.'

Something in the young man's tone worried Galbraith. Gone was the politeness and military efficiency of their first encounter and in its place was a controlled insolence. For the first time he realized just how precarious his position was: alone, at night, surrounded by as vicious a band of thugs as anyone could wish to avoid.

'No harm done, laddie.'

The sentry said nothing. His head turned slowly as he watched Galbraith return to his vehicle, and he was still standing in front of the gates when the Chief Inspector restarted the engine. Then he stepped inside the gatehouse, and the gates swung open. He waited until the Land Rover was out of view before speaking into the intercom.

'Gatehouse to Mr Kirby.'

'Kirby here.'

'He's through, but I delayed him a good few minutes.'

'Good work. I'll see you get relieved shortly.'

*

Kirby smiled at Braxton. 'Our men have at least a quarter of an hour's start on him; more than enough time to set up the listening post.'

'They'll hear everything?'

'All you need is a clear line on his office window. The laser picks up vocal vibrations and sends them to a computer, and that converts them back into language. Foolproof.'

'Excellent. I want to know what that little Scots bastard is up to then . . .' He glanced at Sir Marcus, who was sitting quietly watching them, then added, 'Our friend Superintendent Johnstone may have to do a little more to earn his retirement pay.'

The station was almost deserted when Galbraith returned. He walked quickly to his office to search his IN tray for the notice about the missing soldier. There was a contact number at the bottom of the page. He looked at his wall clock: it was just after ten. Shrugging his shoulders, he began to dial.

'Ministry of Defence, how can I help you?'

'Chief Inspector Galbraith, Highlands Police, stationed at Bannock, near Inverness. I need some information on a missing soldier: Staff Sergeant Mark Fraser . . .'

The tunnel was wide enough for him to scramble along it on hands and knees. Cold was his big enemy now: a sharp draught was blowing into his face and, though it gave him hope that he was near the surface, it was cutting through his thinly clad body. He had already ripped off the edge of his shirt to make a makeshift hat; otherwise nine-tenths of his body heat would escape from the top of his head. He had eaten the last of his meagre rations and knew he would have to find warmth and food soon or risk the danger of wind chill and hypothermia. He was thankful for the increased space as it enabled him to move more of his body and kept him warmer.

For over an hour he climbed steadily upwards along the passage. It twisted and turned every four or five feet, first left, then right, but always upwards. He groped for his torch to have a look ahead and, just before he switched it on, saw one of the most wonderful sights in his life. The stars. Not more than ten feet away the tunnel emerged from the hillside. He scrambled towards the exit.

In his haste he bumped headlong into a metal grille and let out a howl of pain and surprise. He placed both hands against it and heaved. It gave slightly. Perhaps because the builders had believed that the tunnel did not lead to the main chamber or, more likely, because it was directly exposed to the elements, it was not as well secured as the others he had encountered. Leaning his back against the tunnel wall, he kicked it: once, twice. At the third kick the grille collapsed.

Fraser stuck his head out cautiously, feeling the bite of the night wind on his face. He was near the top of the outer rim of the natural amphitheatre, with the main entrance to the potholes entrance directly below him. He pulled himself out, crawled swiftly upwards to the rim and rolled over the edge. He lay on his back staring up at the clear night sky, relief pulsing through him. He hadn't felt this good since he passed Selection.

The bitter cold dragged him back to the present. What to do now? He still had a pistol. He pulled it from the top of his boot and shoved it down the front of his waistband. His thoughts turned involuntarily to Lindsey, but he pushed them aside; that path would lead to anger. There would be time for that when this was over.

He heard a sound. Someone was trying to approach his position stealthily and making a poor job of it. Even a child playing cowboys and Indians should have learnt to roll his feet when near an enemy position, so as to deaden the sound.

Fraser could hear breathing now, sharp intakes, followed by noisy exhalation. Everything he had seen from his opponents marked them out as experts – but this one wasn't. He turned silently on to his stomach and watched. Before long he detected movement. A darkly clad figure was coming up the far side, from the direction of McLeod House.

Groping in his pocket, he found a coin. When the approaching figure was about three feet away he flicked it about five feet in front of him, where it landed on a stone with a satisfying clink. The man turned, his hand going under his jacket to a shoulder holster. Fraser was on him in a second, his left arm tightening around his throat, his right grabbing for the gun hand.

His forearm encountered the soft, firm swell of a feminine breast. He hesitated. She jabbed backwards with her elbow, aiming for the pit of his stomach, and slammed into the pistol in his waistband. The woman gave a stifled scream and tried to stamp on his shin with her right foot. He dodged it easily but was impressed all the same. Someone had taken the time to teach her self-defence, at least. She was gathering herself for another strike when a voice from the darkness froze them both.

'Hold it, you're covered.'

Fraser cursed to himself. He had forgotten the two ridge sentries. His opponent stopped struggling but did not reply to the American. Fraser made an instant decision: the enemy of my enemy is my friend. He released his hold on the young woman, who took a half-step forward and to his left. Fraser sank to one knee.

'Who's there? Step forward and be recognized.' The voice sounded less certain than before.

'I'm lost. Could you direct me to McLeod House?' The woman spoke, her tone firm and unwavering.

Fraser liked the sound of that voice. He could see the sentry clearly now, silhouetted against the skyline. The woman walked forward, the sound of her footsteps covering his own movement, allowing him to sink on to his stomach.

'Who are you, miss?'

'My name's Charlotte Reynolds. I'm a guest of Mr Braxton. I went out walking and got lost.'

The sentry moved towards her. Fraser rose silently behind him and swung the butt of his automatic, hitting him just below the left ear. He caught the body as it dropped and lowered it gently to the ground. Then he stood to observe his new acquaintance. She had her own gun out now, holding it in both hands, barrel pointing downwards.

He recognized the practised combat pistol stance. Right leg forward, slightly bent, taking most of her body weight; left leg nearly straight, left foot at almost forty-five degrees to the right, providing stability. Right hand holding the pistol, right arm straight. Left arm bent, left hand holding the right. It had been devised by a Texas Ranger and was taught in basic training by almost every elite service in the Western world.

In the dim light he could see her features. Staring back at him was an attractive face, more confused than frightened. Eventually the young woman raised her eyes to his and spoke. 'Who the hell are you?'

15

Fraser bent and removed the unconscious sentry's jacket. He slipped the padded parka over his chilled body, then undid the man's boots, removed them and used the laces to tie his hands behind his back. When he looked up briefly he saw that the young woman was still poised, her pistol at the ready. 'If you're not going to use that, put it away,' he told her.

He continued to secure the sentry, then gagged him with his own handkerchief. He glanced at Charlotte again; she had holstered her automatic. He gave her a nod of encouragement, dragged the sentry to his feet and hoisted him up in a fireman's lift. Without looking to see if she would follow, he picked up the rifle and headed for the observation post. He found it without difficulty and dumped the sentry in the corner. The small bunker was expertly cut into the side of the hill and gave an excellent view of the surrounding area. There was a small stove for heat and, glory of glories, food and coffee just prepared.

Fraser was relishing his first taste of hot food and drink in days when Charlotte came in and stared at him but said nothing. When he had finished and was pouring himself a second cup of coffee he nodded towards the sentry and said, 'These people have been trying to kill me for the last three days.'

'Why are you here?'

'I might ask you the same question. Let's see, you're not Special Branch, wrong gun, nor are you MI5.' He contemplated her for a second. 'SIS?'

She gave a slight nod and her mouth twisted into a wry smile. 'Everybody I meet seems to be able to spot who my employers are.'

'Where were you trained: the Fort?'

'How did you . . .?' she asked, for the nickname for the training centre for MI5 and SIS agents was known to only a few.

'That's not important,' he said. 'I got here by accident. My wife and I were on a climbing holiday . . .' He told his story briefly and without emotion, watching first shock, then disbelief and finally sorrow wash over the woman's lovely face.

'For a long time I didn't know even my name,' he then added. 'I guess a part of me wanted to erase the memory of Lindsey's death. For most of the time I was operating on pure instinct.'

'You must have some instincts.'

He allowed himself a tired smile. 'I've been a soldier for sixteen years. Ulster, the Falklands, the Gulf and Bosnia. I guess I was the right man in the wrong place at the wrong time.'

She nodded. She wanted to say something comforting about his wife, but words were inadequate. Instead she smiled and reached out to touch his arm. He acknowledged the gesture with a slight dip of his head.

'I still don't know why. Why they killed Lindsey. Why the lead-lined cave.'

Charlotte looked into the night. 'I don't know why they

killed your wife, but I can explain the cave. The man who owns this estate, Edward Braxton, also owns and operates five nuclear power plants in the States. About a year ago there were reports of an accident at one of them, and it was shut down for a while. When investigators from the US Energy Commission arrived they found everything in order. Braxton's people told them the plant had been shut down for a training exercise – some sort of simulated accident. But there were persistent rumours that they'd been experimenting with a new kind of reactor which had overheated and that several employees had been killed. The Energy Commission was planning a detailed investigation to start this month.'

Fraser saw the anger in Charlotte's face.

'We believe they were trying to install a new type of reactor that hadn't received clearance. It went haywire. They only just avoided a meltdown.'

Charlotte took a deep breath before continuing. 'They anaged to dismantle the new generator ahead of the investigation, but we think they must have been left with some highly toxic waste to dispose of.'

'Ragnarök.'

'What?'

'Oh, just something I read about once. One of the Norse myths. The final battle between good and evil.'

'Yeah, that's about the size of it. For Braxton the whole business has been a bigger problem than you can imagine,' Charlotte said grimly. 'He was faced with potentially crippling sanctions if the American authorities found out. It would've cost him billions in clean-up costs and fines. Even he wasn't about to spend that sort of money.'

'Why didn't he just dump it at sea?'

Charlotte made a face. 'He would've done if he could've

got away with it, but my guess is he didn't have time. It's not easy stuff to move. All nuclear waste shipments are swarming with federal armed guards. My SIS controller has been keeping an eye on Braxton for several years, but nothing could ever be proved. A source inside Braxton Industries told us he'd managed to get the waste out of the country by mixing it in with a consignment of spent fuel rods. That man was found floating face up in New York Harbour.

'My controller suspected that Braxton intended to separate the waste from the fuel rods in UK Customs, but he didn't know for sure. Braxton has contacts in the civil service and intelligence community, people who owed him favours from the Cold War days. And he definitely bribed others.'

'How did you come to be up here?'

'A top Customs official called Carter contacted my controller and gave him an outline of what Braxton was up to. My controller couldn't trust any of his regular agents, so I was recruited direct from training.'

'And did you make contact with Carter?'

'He was killed, apparently in a burglary at his home in London. But I've met someone in the local police here, Chief Inspector Galbraith, who firmly believes Carter was killed on this estate.'

'Can you trust him?'

Charlotte smiled. She told him about Hamilton and Anne, and Anne's letter to Galbraith.

Fraser nodded slowly, lost in thought. 'Sounds like a good man. What about you, how much back-up have you got?'

'Almost none,' Charlotte said, laughing. For a second she looked totally vulnerable. 'I'm really out of my depth . . . I came up here hoping to get some photographic proof and take it direct to a ministerial contact in the cabinet. We've got to move quickly. If he gets the nuclear waste into that chamber we'll never prove a thing. It's my guess that the entire complex has been wired with explosives. Once he gets the waste inside he'll bury it under tons of rock.'

Fraser thought back to the main tunnel shaft and nodded. 'I've seen the demolition charges.' He paused. 'Forget the photographs. McLeod House – the proof you need is in there. We'll head over there tomorrow, but now I need sleep.'

There was a soft moan from the sentry. The young man eyed Fraser with a mixture of fear and hatred.

Fraser returned the stare unflinchingly, then walked over to him. 'I'm the man you've been hunting these last three days.' His tone was soft, almost conversational. 'I'm going to remove your gag. If you scream or call out, I will kill you. Understand?'

The sentry nodded slowly. He coughed as the makeshift gag was removed, and made as if to speak.

Fraser put a finger to his lips. 'Just answer my questions. What's your name?'

'Go to hell.'

Fraser shook his head. 'Not before I've sent you there first.' He shoved the barrel of his automatic into the sentry's mouth and eased the hammer back with his thumb. The click as it fell into place made the man's eyes bulge.

'Duane.'

'Good,' said Fraser, nodding with satisfaction. 'Now, Duane, there's an easy way and a hard way.'

Duane's eyes never left Fraser's face.

Fraser's voice remained low as he continued. 'The easy way is, you tell me when you're going to get relieved and we all get a good night's sleep. Then tomorrow, when your relief arrives, I give him a tap on the head and leave you both here until after all this is over. The hard way is that you stay silent, I put this gag back on you, muffle this pistol and shoot you dead. Then I kill your friend when he turns up.'

Charlotte had absolutely no doubt that Fraser would do exactly as he said. The sentry was convinced too. 'How do I know you won't just kill me anyway?'

'You don't,' Fraser replied matter of factly. 'But you can be sure I'll kill you if you don't talk.'

The sentry hesitated another few seconds, his eyes frantically appealing to Charlotte for help. He looked like some trapped animal. She felt sympathy for him, then remembered Fraser's wife and unborn child lying dead and cold in a body bag. Her face hardened. It was enough to convince Duane.

'OK. OK, you win,' he said to Fraser. 'My relief is due at ten o'clock sharp, tomorrow morning.'

'Good. What about radio calls. How often do you have to report in?'

'I don't. They think you're dead. There's just a listening watch for emergencies.'

Fraser allowed himself a smile. 'Better and better.' He shoved the gag back into Duane's mouth and put an almost fatherly hand on his shoulder.

'Now, I'm a very, very light sleeper, and if you so much as twitch a face muscle in the next three hours I might think you're trying to break free and kill me. And that'll almost certainly mean I'll shoot you. OK?'

The young American's eyes showed that he understood perfectly.

'Good. Get some sleep – you look tired.'

Fraser gave him a friendly pat on the cheek, then turned back to Charlotte and winked. He unrolled the sentry's sleeping bag, climbed in and placed the rifle and pistol within reach, his hands across his chest, and closed his eyes.

'I hope you don't mind me taking the bed?' he whispered.

'Not at all,' said Charlotte.

'Good. I'll wake at eight and we'll prepare for our guests at ten.'

In seconds Charlotte heard his breathing become soft and deep. She studied him as he slept. He was probably in his late thirties, just under six feet tall and, she had noticed, had a lean, hard-muscled body and broad shoulders. His face interested her. In sleep the fatigue and sorrow washed away, leaving the face of a man of character and strength. There were laughter lines at the corners of his eyes and mouth; it was a face most women would find interesting rather than attractive. She wanted to learn more about the man. As she watched his face it became troubled again. He was clearly having a bad dream. His lips moved and as she bent closer she heard him whisper, over and over again, 'Lindsey'.

Moved by compassion, she touched his brow with her fingertips. Instantly his eyes opened, focused on her and then closed once more. She drew back, and as she did so she noticed that the sentry was already asleep.

Quietly, she made herself comfortable in the opposite corner. But sleep would not come: too much had happened in such a short time. Her eyes were drawn to Fraser again; even in the semi-darkness the scar from the bullet wound that had so nearly killed him was clearly visible.

She thought about the story he had told her, of the men he had killed over the past three days and the terrible loss he had suffered. She could recognize the hurt inside him, and more than that, something that frightened her: an awful controlled rage. She reflected that the US Energy Commission would be the least of Braxton's worries once Fraser caught up with him. For some perverse reason the thought comforted her. She drifted off to sleep with a smile on her face.

A noise woke her, and for a second she didn't know where she was. For a moment anxiety threatened to overwhelm her as she studied the unfamiliar surroundings. Then her memory flooded back. She sat up and peered at her watch in the gloomy half-light. It was still long before dawn. What had woken her? Again she heard a soft, heart-rending moan. Rising silently, she stepped over the still sleeping Duane to where Fraser lay curled up in the foetal position.

She could tell he was dreaming again: every so often a moan escaped his lips. As she watched, a single tear rolled down the side of his face. She slipped on to the bed beside him and drew her blanket over them both. Fraser's eyes opened immediately, his lips moving in an unspoken question. She put her finger against his lips, then cradled his head against her breast. In a second sleep claimed him again; this time it was not interrupted by troubled dreams.

The Land Rover bounced along the makeshift track towards the potholes. Its four occupants looked tired. The party had started at the Marquis of Montrose and finished at around two-thirty back at McLeod House. The driver feared his head would explode and his three relief sentries felt just as bad. Two of them were throwing up over the tailboard as he drove, one hand to his brow. His front-seat passenger was slumped in the corner, huddled in his coat and shivering uncontrollably. As they hit a particularly bad bump he groaned. The driver glanced at him. 'You look like shit,' he said.

'I feel worse. I should have laid off the whisky.'

The driver felt his stomach churn. 'You better believe it,

buddy. They ain't been brewing that stuff for hundreds of years for nothing.'

The entrance to the natural amphitheatre that housed the potholes loomed up ahead and the driver pulled up, whereupon his passenger half fell, half rolled out of the front seat. As he lowered the back to allow the other two to disembark, he could hear retching and managed a smile even though his own stomach was churning.

'OK, ladies, end of the line. Up and at 'em.'

There were low growls of protest as they pulled out their kit.

'Jesus, this is all I need,' the front-seat passenger grumbled to no one in particular. 'Twenty-four hours in a freezing observation post.'

'Think about that bonus, Schwartz – that should make the time go a little faster.'

The driver ignored the man's observations on Braxton's parentage, went back to his seat and watched as the two men separated and trudged up the hill to their posts. His third passenger would relieve the guard at the pothole entrance.

Schwartz was stumbling, and stopped every few yards to retch or vomit. As he neared the observation point he pulled his water bottle from his belt and took a long swig. He wiped his mouth with the back of his hand and shouted irritably, 'Duane, where the hell are you?'

He got no reply and felt his temper rise. Duane was clearly asleep, couldn't even get himself out of bed to be relieved of duty. The sentry stormed up to the camouflage netting and raised it to one side. Sure enough, there was the lazy bastard, slumped forward with his head resting on his arms. He strode forward and grasped him by the shoulder. 'Come on, you sonofabitch, wake up. You're . . .'

The words died in his throat as he saw that Duane was gagged and tied. Before he could react he felt the cold muzzle of a gun at his neck and a calm, authoritative voice in his ear.

'If you don't want to spend the next two hours unconscious and wake up with a nasty headache, drop your gun slowly to the floor.'

Schwartz did exactly as he was told – his head hurt enough as it was.

The driver saw Duane coming down the hill towards him and grunted with relief. As soon as the other one appeared he could drop off the last guard and get back to the house and grab some sleep. His head still hurt like a bitch. He shoved it out of the window.

'Move it up, man. We ain't got all day.'

Duane gave him a wave and headed for the back of the Land Rover. The driver was surprised: the youngster always liked to sit in the front. He felt the back of the vehicle dip slightly as Duane clambered in.

'What's the matter – tired of riding up front?'

There was a noise like a butcher's cleaver hitting raw meat, then a soft grunt.

'What the fuck . . .?'

He spun round to see the rifle heading for his head and had just enough time to jerk away, avoiding the full force of the impact. Instead the butt caught him a glancing blow against his cheek and dazed him. Feeling behind him for the door handle, he tumbled backwards out on to the hard ground. He stared up at the dark-faced demon with the blazing blue eyes.

Without thinking, he aimed a ferocious kick at Fraser's groin and got the rifle butt against his knee for his pains. He let out a howl, which was cut short as the butt crashed against his jaw. He wouldn't have to worry about his hangover for an hour or two.

Fraser crouched over the body, his rifle clutched in both hands, butt into his shoulder. He was worried that the driver's shout might have been heard. He stood, surveying the area. The returning sentry must not see anything out of place. He hooked his rifle over his shoulder and bent to grasp the driver by the shoulders.

'Just stay like that, bud. Don't move a muscle.' The voice came from behind him. A quiet, confident, American voice. Fraser froze.

'Good. Now drop that rifle.'

Fraser started to comply.

'Slowly now, like molasses in winter, or I'll drill you for sure.'

Fraser eased the rifle from his shoulder and spread his arms wide.

'Now turn round, real slow – no sudden movements. I got a real itchy finger.'

Fraser turned. The last sentry stood by the rear of the Land Rover, his AK47 at the ready. He was a shortish, powerfully built man in his early thirties, with the blond, close-cropped hair of a US Marine. They eyed each other.

'You that limey we been chasing for three days?'

Fraser nodded.

A grin spread across the sentry's face. 'Whew, boy, have I hit the jackpot! Braxton wants you real bad.' But there was no joy in his eyes. 'And you have no idea what Mr Kirby plans to do with you. No, sirree – no idea at all.'

Fraser noticed a movement. Charlotte emerged silently from a low clump of bushes, her automatic pistol grasped in both hands.

He spoke quickly to distract the sentry. 'Do you think you'll get away with all of this: all these deaths, Operation Hades . . .?'

The man's eyes narrowed. 'What do you know about Hades?'

'Everything, and so do the security services. Christ, man, do you think I'm here by coincidence?'

Uncertainty crossed the sentry's face. Charlotte was directly behind him now.

'Don't matter who knows what. Ol' man Braxton, he has more money than God. He'll buy his way out of this and he'll be real generous to the man who brings you in.'

'Drop it!' Charlotte shouted.

The sentry's shoulders hunched at the sound, then he threw a quick look over his shoulder and the smile returned. 'Hell, girl, you gave me a real scare there.'

Fraser took a step towards his rifle.

The sentry's head whipped round. 'Hold it. Move another muscle and you're a dead man.'

Fraser froze again.

Without taking his eyes off Fraser, the sentry addressed Charlotte. 'Well, little girl, we got what us Americans call a Mexican stand-off. You shoot me and I'll kill Mr Fraser here. That's your name, boy, ain't it – Fraser?'

Fraser returned his stare. 'That's right. The young lady is an SIS agent, just looking for an excuse to kill you. Why don't you drop the rifle, soldier?'

The sentry shook his head slowly. 'If you had the gun I would, but not her. She don't have it in her. Now, little lady, I'm gonna count to five and if you ain't dropped that big old pistol by then I'm gonna kill Mr Fraser here. Do you understand me?'

Fraser looked at Charlotte. She was chalk white, her hands trembling.

The sentry began his count. 'One.'

'Shoot him, Charlotte,' Fraser urged.

'Shut up. Two.'

'For God's sake, shoot him.'

'I told you to . . .'

There was a single shot. The thought flashed through his mind that the sentry had fired. He waited for the numbing impact, followed by searing pain as the bullet ripped through his body. There was none.

The American's face held a look of astonishment. His camouflaged grey-green field jacket was slowly turning scarlet. He looked down at his chest, then raised his fingers to his face and stared with fascination at the blood. He seemed totally absorbed, but then remembered Fraser and, focusing his eyes on him, reached down to grasp his rifle more securely. His right hand closed over the stock of the AK47; it was suddenly too heavy for him to hold. It dropped to his side, dangling from his hand. The strength left his legs and he pitched forward on to his knees. For a moment he retained hold of the weapon, then it fell from his nerveless fingers. Without turning his head, he spoke to Charlotte.

'I didn't think you had it in you, girlie . . . I honestly didn't.'

The words ended in a gurgling sigh as he fell on to his face, blood oozing from his mouth, and lay still.

Fraser heard a choking cry and saw Charlotte drop her pistol and throw her hands up to her face. He walked to the sentry, bent down and felt for the man's pulse. He had lost two good friends who had been shot by terrorists they thought were dead. But this guy would never trouble anyone again.

He walked to Charlotte's side, picked up her gun and handed it to her. She shook her head violently. Fraser slung his rifle and grabbed her by the shoulders.

'Listen to me,' he growled.

She stared fixedly at the dead man. He shook her roughly and repeated his command.

This time she turned towards him and he said, more gently now, 'It was him or us, understand? You did the right thing, OK?'

For a second her eyes remained unfocused. 'I killed him . . . I . . .' It was a low, soft cry and at any other time Fraser would have cradled her in his arms.

'Yes, you killed him, to stop him killing me. Now snap out of it' – he shook her once more – 'because I need you. Do you understand? I need you.' He forced the gun back into her hand and walked back towards the dead man. 'Come on, help me move him.'

For a second she hesitated, then shoved the pistol into her shoulder holster and helped him to drag the sentry into the cover of a nearby clump of bushes. Then she was violently sick. Fraser ignored her and concentrated on concealing the body. She stood and faced him. Fraser noticed that the colour was coming back into her cheeks. He gave her a nod of encouragement and turned to go back to the Land Rover. Together they pushed it off the road.

'I'm hoping when they find this they'll think I'm still in the area. It's too risky to try using the roads. We'll head straight across country. With any luck we'll be at McLeod House before the alarm has been raised and this will act as a diversion. What time are you due to contact Galbraith?'

She checked her watch. 'Just over an hour.'

'Good. We should be in position by then.'

As they were about to start off towards the woods Charlotte put a hand on his arm. 'Thanks for what you said: about needing me.'

'No need for thanks,' he replied as he unslung his rifle. 'It was true.'

16

Fraser set a blistering pace through the woods, only stopping to listen now and then to a radio he'd taken from one of the sentries. So far the men he and Charlotte had ambushed had not been discovered. But the calls from their colleagues were becoming more strident by the minute and it could only be a matter of time before they were on the couple's heels.

Pausing in a small natural clearing, Fraser peered ahead through the closely packed trees. Some way beyond them he could see open ground. 'We'll rest here for a few minutes. As near as I can figure out, McLeod House is only about two hundred yards that way.' He pointed ahead and to his left. They were the first words he had spoken to his companion since they had left the potholes.

Stifling a moan of relief, Charlotte collapsed against a tree. A gentle breeze wafted a stray hair into her eyes and stuck it to her sweat-covered face. She brushed it away irritably and rummaged in her pockets for a handkerchief to mop her brow, then lifted the neck of her thick woollen jumper to allow the air to cool her body. Feeling slightly better, she looked across at Fraser, who was sitting against a tree, studying the ground ahead. She noticed he wasn't sweating, or even breathing heavily.

'Don't you ever get tired?' she snapped.

He turned his head to glance at her, then resumed his watch. 'Sorry, but we haven't the luxury of time on our side,' he replied, his voice was barely above a whisper.

Charlotte felt disconcerted by his lack of warmth, especially after the previous night. She had woken to find him already preparing for the arrival of Duane's relief; he had managed to extricate himself from her arms without disturbing her. Now she studied him again as he sat absorbed in his own thoughts. Even in the short time she had known him she felt fascinated by this strange, lonely man.

She realized that in her present situation she was bound to be attracted to a powerful man who could protect her, yet she had seen this one at his most vulnerable and knew the depths of his despair at the loss of his wife and unborn child. Like the previous night, she longed to reach out to him, to help in some way, to heal him. She searched for something to say but just then the radio burst into excited chatter. The relief sentries had been found. There were frantic cries for assistance.

Fraser was on his feet instantly; the moment was gone. 'Good, they're sending more men from the house. That should make our job easier. Isn't it about time you called your policeman?'

Charlotte pulled the two-way radio from inside her coat. 'Ian, this is Charlotte. Over.'

'Roger, Charlotte. You're smack on time.'

'Ian, things are worse here than I thought . . .' Swiftly she outlined her meeting with Fraser.

'Christ. What do you want me to do: come and pick you up?'

'Not yet. Fraser reckons he can get us into McLeod House. We still have no definite proof, but if we can gain access we may be able to find enough proof to hang Braxton.'

'Are you crazy? I'm coming for you straight away.'

Charlotte smiled at his concern. 'Don't worry,' she told him quietly.

Galbraith was not reassured. 'I think we're well past the worrying stage. What do you want me to do?'

'Pick us up at the main gate. That will mean you getting inside and neutralizing the gate sentry. Can you organize that?'

Galbraith's face creased into a smile. 'I'll be there. What time?'

Charlotte looked up at Fraser. 'What time do you want your chauffeur?'

Fraser looked at his watch. 'If we're not at the main gate in three hours, we'll never be there.'

When she spoke again her voice sounded less certain. 'Three hours exactly, Ian.'

Galbraith checked the station clock. 'Three hours it is. And, Charlotte, be careful . . .'

Fraser checked his rifle and handgun. 'Let's go,' he said, without looking back.

Galbraith switched off the radio and lifted the phone. 'Angus, I want two squad cars and six uniformed PCs in the briefing room in two hours for a special operation. Make sure Sergeant Hutton and PC Clarke are among them.'

Angus started to protest, but Galbraith cut in abruptly. 'I know it's their day off. Get them in, it's important. Pull in any off-duty personnel if you have to, but make sure they're here.' He plonked down the receiver to avoid further discussion.

The ultrasonic direct line-of-sight laser transmitter, known as the LT in security circles, was the crowning glory of listening devices. It had been developed by the CIA in the late eighties and used by them to eavesdrop on Soviet consulates and embassies around the world.

Like all remarkable inventions, the LT was beautifully simple. A laser beam, connected to and controlled by a digital computer, was directed at a window. When anyone in the room under surveillance spoke, the pane of glass vibrated and the vibrations were fed to a computer which converted them back into speech. The device had its drawbacks: the operators had to have a direct line of sight to their target and fog and rain adversely affected its performance. Even so, it was the fastest and most efficient method of eavesdropping on a building ever developed.

An unmarked blue Escort van was parked less than fifty yards from the police station. The two men inside directed the very latest LT equipment at the window of Galbraith's office, through a hole so small that it was undetectable to the naked eye. The Chief Inspector's entire conversation was transmitted instantly, via a coded radio channel, to Kirby's operations room at McLeod House.

'Fraser alive. What do I have to do to kill that man?' Kirby jumped to his feet. 'How many men do we have here right now?' The radio operator, a burly New Orleans Creole, looked up through a haze of cigarette smoke.

'Weaver and four others,' he answered.

'Tell them to kit up and meet me in the entrance hall straight away. Don't use the radio. He probably took another from the sentries he left at the potholes.'

Kirby looked across at Braxton. 'I want something done about Galbraith now.' Before his boss could reply, he was leaving the room, cursing to himself.

Fraser moved more cautiously, scanning the ground ahead before moving, his rifle tight into his shoulder, moving constantly from side to side. He held up a hand, sank on to one knee and motioned for Charlotte to close up on him. She had her own pistol out in front of her, gripped in both hands. She leaned forward to catch his words.

'They'll probably have sentries around the house. If we meet one, just sit tight. I'll deal with him.'

Charlotte nodded in reply, her heart thumping against her chest. The mixture of fear and excitement was making it difficult to breathe, let alone speak. Fraser rose to his feet and moved forward noiselessly. She watched him for a moment. His presence made her feel safe, even as another part of her understood the danger they were in. Then the forest in front of them erupted in a cacophony of noise, flashes and smoke.

Fraser dropped to one knee, firing short, controlled bursts. Charlotte was paralysed with fear as bullets slapped against the trees around her, and whined into the distance. Fraser let off another burst, then ran backwards three or four steps to kneel beside her. Immediately he fired yet again and for the first time she saw what he was aiming at.

A line of figures was advancing towards them, firing as they went. They were never visible for more than a couple of seconds. Three rounds slammed into the tree next to her, showering her with splinters of bark. She tried to scream, but found she couldn't.

Beside her Fraser sighted carefully and fired. One of the darting figures rose up. Charlotte had an impression of round, staring eyes in a young face, a mouth open in a noiseless scream, a green combat jacket, marred by a tattoo of red dots across its front. Then Fraser's hand was on her shoulder and she found herself being dragged backwards. She looked hard at him. His face was set. He spared her a glance.

'For God's sake, run when I run,' he rasped.

Behind them there were shouts and the firing slackened momentarily. They staggered forward half a dozen paces, Fraser with one hand on Charlotte's shoulder. Then he stopped, turned and pushed her down on to one knee. Bullets were still whistling around them but even to Charlotte's untrained ears the firing sounded less intense.

Fraser fired again, standing this time, his arm braced against a tree. Then he knelt swiftly to change magazines before firing again in short, sharp bursts, his shoulder rocking with the rhythm. He glanced to his right, then knelt swiftly, pushing his face close to hers.

'They've detached some men to flank us to our right. In a few seconds they'll have us in a cross-fire. We have to run fast and keep running until I tell you to stop.'

Charlotte nodded.

Fraser fired two long bursts, one to the front, the other to his right. 'Now!' he yelled.

His voice galvanized her into action: she was on her feet, head down, running flat out, her arms pumping. She was aware of Fraser just behind her and she heard the howls of their hunters as they realized what was happening. The forest echoed to cascades of rapid automatic fire. She seemed to be moving in slow motion, her legs leaden but her arms flailing in frantic double time. Her lungs burnt from lack of oxygen. Flashes of light darted behind her eyes, and the woodland around her was alternately dazzlingly bright and dull. She felt on the verge of unconsciousness as Fraser's hand clamped on to her shoulder. Her feet continued forward and she sat down with a bump. Fraser knelt beside her, his chest heaving. He grinned.

'Boy, can you run,' he gasped, drawing in huge gulps of air. 'They're not far behind. We haven't much time.'

He rose and pulled her to her feet like a rag doll and half pulled, half carried her forward. After a few dozen paces he stopped at a dirt track which carved its way through the forest in front of them. Turning right, he almost galloped along the side of the track until he found what he was looking for. Burrowing under the track was a drainage ditch, half full of dirt-black water. The end nearest them was clogged with debris, the other end clear. He shoved her unceremoniously into it, then uprooted a small fir tree, threw it down after her and dropped into the ditch himself.

'I'm going to lead them away from you, then double back and pick you up. If I'm not back in an hour, make your way to the front gate and RV with Galbraith. I'll be there if I miss you here. OK?'

She nodded.

'Remember, stay perfectly quiet for at least an hour and you should be safe.'

As he started to rise she grabbed his hand. She tried to speak, but found she couldn't. His eyes held hers for just a second, his features softened, making him look boyish, then a faint smile crossed his lips as he kissed her lightly on the forehead.

Charlotte found her voice. 'Why did you do that?'

'No reason – you just looked like you needed it.'

A wave of emotion surged through her. Involuntarily she threw her arms around him, enjoying the feel of the hard warmth of his body against hers. She felt the comforting touch of his hand stroking her hair and turned her head to look into those wonderful blue eyes of his. He untangled her arms from around his shoulders and held her hands briefly in his. 'Don't worry,' he whispered.

She heard a faint shout behind her and glanced over her shoulder. When she looked back he was gone. She pulled the uprooted fir tree into the mouth of the ditch. It blocked out most of the light and she felt a momentary wave of panic.

She heard another shout before the firing started again, then the sound of bodies crashing through the trees, screams of pain and defiance. She clasped her ears, fighting the impulse to scream but sobbing silently with a mixture of relief and fear. Eventually the noise subsided.

Cramp began to grip her legs and back; she was kneeling with her back jammed against the chilling wet stone. The pain in her lower back became more intense. She tried repeatedly to shift position, but her movements only made her wetter and colder.

Something plopped in the water behind her, and she scrambled for the exit. Pushing the fir tree aside, she stood up cautiously, relief coursing through her as she straightened and stretched her arms.

'So you decided to visit us after all, Miss Reynolds.'

She froze, then turned slowly. Kirby sat with his back against a tree, a cigar clamped between his teeth. His face was tinged with grey and it was easy to see why: his left arm was supported in a bloody makeshift sling. His right, steady as a rock, held a Glock 9mm automatic pistol. It was pointing straight at her.

Galbraith assembled everything he thought he would need. Spread out on the briefing room table were a megaphone, a pair of huge bolt cutters, seven personal radios and four CS gas sprays which had only recently been issued for test and evaluation. He'd thought it absurd at the time but was glad of them now. Also on the table were two old bolt-action .303 Lee Enfield rifles and three Smith and Wesson .38 revolvers – all the fire-power the station possessed.

He picked up one of the Lee Enfields and sighted along the barrel. The last time it had been used was over ten years earlier, to shoot a bull that had gone haywire at a county fair. Only himself, Sergeant Hutton and PC Clarke were firearm-trained. Knowing what they were going up against, he hoped to hell they didn't have to use them.

Behind him the briefing room door opened. He turned.

'You're early, Angus. Are all the men assembled? I was just . . .'

The words died in his throat. Standing in the doorway was Superintendent Johnstone. He caught a glimpse of the anxious faces of Angus and PC Lang hovering behind him. Johnstone tapped his mobile phone against his leg, then said, 'Send the off-duty personnel home, Sergeant, and the rest of the men back out on patrol. PC Lang, wait outside this door until I call you.'

He stepped inside and pulled the door firmly closed. Galbraith watched him walk around the table, place his mobile phone next to the radios and settle himself on one of the chairs laid out for the briefing. Johnstone studied the large-scale map of McLeod House that had been pinned to the blackboard then turned his gaze on Galbraith.

'Well, Chief Inspector?'

'I have information that a major crime is in process at McLeod House. It is my intention to investigate.'

'I see. And where did you get this information?'

For some insane reason, the story he had told PC Lang about the bird flying north for the winter flashed into his mind. 'I'm afraid I can't answer that question at this time, sir.'

Johnstone pursed his lips. 'Very well, Chief Inspector. So what crime do you suspect is taking place on the McLeod estate?'

'I'm afraid, sir, I can't reveal that either.'

Johnstone stood and walked the short distance to stand directly in front of Galbraith. 'Let me see if I've got this right. You're about to launch an armed raid on the home of a prominent member of this community, based on information you can't or won't reveal, about a crime you can't or won't specify.' He paused. 'Doesn't sound too good does it, Chief Inspector?'

Galbraith pulled a cigarette from his pocket and lit it, inhaling deeply and blowing the smoke between them.

'When you put it like that, no, it doesn't.'

Johnstone winced at the smoke. 'I'd like to say that this gives me no pleasure, but I'd be lying. I've never liked you, Galbraith. It's my belief that you're having a nervous breakdown, brought on by grief over the death of your former partner. In the circumstances, I'm placing you under arrest for your own protection until you can be medically examined. PC Lang' – Johnstone waited until the worried-looking constable stepped into the room – 'escort the Chief Inspector to the cells. He's under arrest for his own protection and is not to be left unattended until the medical officer arrives.'

'I'd like to call the Chief Constable,' Galbraith said.

Johnstone paused just long enough to look as though he was considering the request. 'I'm afraid I've already called him and he has, with great reluctance, endorsed my decision.'

Galbraith leaned towards Johnstone, so that his voice could only be heard by his superior. 'You won't get away with this, you bastard.'

Johnstone replied in the same tone. 'I already have.'

Galbraith locked eyes with the taller man before turning to follow Lang from the room. As they stepped into the corridor Johnstone's voice echoed after them.

'Remember, PC Lang, he's not to be left alone.'

Galbraith allowed himself to be guided by the grey-faced young officer along the twisting corridor which he knew so well until they reached the cells at the rear of the station: two chilly concrete rooms with inch-thick steel doors. Galbraith stopped and looked at Lang, fully aware of the apparent stupidity of what he was about to say.

'I know you're not going to believe this, but if you put me in those cells you'll be sentencing two good people to death.'

'The Superintendent says you've gone crazy, chief.'

'What do you think, laddie?'

Lang looked at the cell door and back to Galbraith.

'I think I'd like to learn from that bloody bird you told me about. I can't say anything if I'm unconscious.' He closed his eyes and thrust his chin forward. 'Make it look good.'

Galbraith patted the young PC on the shoulder with his left hand. 'If I get out of this, Lang lad, I swear I'll make you a sergeant.' Then he hit him with all the power he had in his right arm. Lang crumpled to the floor. Galbraith rolled him on to his side, removed his belt keys and swiftly unlocked the cell.

After depositing Lang inside he retraced his steps along the dingy corridor. He found the door of the briefing room ajar; the room was empty. From the front office he could hear Johnstone issuing orders. He thought about the firearms and swiftly dismissed the idea: the ammunition was in the front office. Grabbing the bolt cutters, megaphone and a CS spray under one arm, he started for the window. On impulse he pocketed Johnstone's mobile phone.

In seconds he was in the front yard. A police Land Rover stood there, the driver's door ajar and the keys in the ignition. He threw the equipment on to the front passenger seat, clambered in, released the hand brake and rolled soundlessly out of the car park and down the hill. As he drove towards McLeod House he thought over his predicament. Securing the front gate with six uniformed constables had seemed daunting enough. On his own it looked impossible. He checked his watch. Impossible or not, in exactly one hour he had to do it.

Fraser ran three paces, doubled over and spun round to rest his back against a tree. He squatted, resting his rifle between his knees and tried to regulate his breathing. No more than a hundred yards behind him his pursuers were shouting to each other and letting off the occasional shot. As near as he could guess, there were only half a dozen of them. He had definitely hit two; the others were spread out in an extended line. They were shepherding him towards open ground. If there were any more he would be in serious trouble. Sooner or later they would run him into an ambush. He had to slip the net soon, before reinforcements arrived.

He chanced a look around the tree. Barely fifty yards away he could see one of his hunters, his AK47 held high, calling to an unseen figure to his right. He ducked. He had to immobilize the man coming towards him – and quietly. His first thought was his knife, but he soon dropped the idea. It was notoriously hard to kill a man from behind with a knife. The blade was invariably deflected off bone and even if a vital organ was hit, the victim usually lived long enough to scream and struggle. A hand clamped over a mouth was insufficient to gag a man and the noise would be heard many yards away.

He leaned his rifle against a tree and dipped into the top pocket of his combat jacket and extracted a roll of parachute cord and the nylon fishing line. With the first he made two loops for his hands, leaving about eighteen inches between them. Then he tied one end of the fishing line to the branch of a nearby bush, looped it around the tree and squirmed on his stomach to the other side.

Looking through the bushes, he could see the man approaching. He didn't stare at him but kept him in his peripheral vision. When the man neared the tree, Fraser tugged gently on the line. Instantly the man stiffened, pointed his AK47 directly at the bush and began to stalk slowly towards it.

Fraser gathered himself and when the man was two steps past him he rose swiftly to his feet, making no more noise than the passing breeze. Holding the makeshift garrotte above his head, he took a swift step forwards. His target had a half-second of comprehension; maybe he heard a footstep or merely sensed that something was wrong. He spun round.

Fraser's hands smashed down into his chest, driving the air from his lungs, then jerked backwards with all his strength. The paracord bit into the man's neck, crushing the voice box and instantly cutting off all sound from his throat. Fraser crossed his hands, right under left, and there was a light snap as the man fell on to his side. He had used his victim's own body weight to snap his neck.

Fraser moved with him, keeping a tight grip on his garrotte, one knee on his back, head up, alert, in case his attack had been spotted. He waited until he was sure the search line had passed him, then looked down. There was no need to check if the man was dead: the angle of his neck told him everything.

He quickly retrieved his rifle and ran at a crouch back along his tracks. He zigzagged, moving in a circular route but always edging towards where he had left Charlotte. It took him fifteen minutes to reach the spot. He whistled twice before dropping into the ditch, but it was empty. It was a little under an hour since he had left her. Perhaps she had miscalculated the time and left early.

He climbed out of the ditch, noted the discarded fir tree and automatically glanced at the ground around about. A discarded cigar butt caught his eye. He picked it up and smelt it. It was fresh; he could still smell the smoke and feel the warmth.

Then he studied the ground closely. He could plainly see where someone had sat with his – or her – back against the tree: there was something smeared on the bark. He touched his fingers to it and sniffed them. Blood.

He looked in the direction of McLeod House. Where else would they take her?

17

Fraser, knowing shadows gave the best concealment a man could have as long as he remained motionless, stood in the deep shade of a fir tree and studied McLeod House for the first time.

They would want to question Charlotte about him and her mission, he was sure of that. But then what? An image of Lindsey sprang into his mind. Lindsey laughing and joking. Lindsey lying in his arms, her eyes closed, lips parted, waiting for him to kiss her. Lindsey lying cold and still, her face a death-mask. He forced the images aside. It was too late for her. It wasn't too late for Charlotte.

The fortified grey-stone house appeared to be formidable. Video cameras were positioned at the corners of the rect-angular building and another above the main door. The camera at the southern corner, nearest the driveway leading from the main gate, was on a continual sweep which, Fraser calculated, covered an arc of about 180 degrees – enough to scan the open ground, at the top of the driveway, that served as a car park.

He nodded and smiled to himself with satisfaction. Every security system had a flaw, and the mobile camera was this one's Achilles' heel. He timed the scan: exactly fifteen seconds. Next he turned his attention to the driveway. Since

Red Hugh's time the forest had steadily encroached upon the house, but there was still forty yards of open ground between the nearest cover and the granite walls.

At most, he estimated, he had seven to eight seconds to get under the monitor's field of vision. To cover forty yards in seven seconds in normal circumstances wouldn't be too difficult, but now, dressed in heavy clothing and very tired, he didn't know if he could make it. Whichever way he looked at it, it would be tight.

Next he scanned the roof. When the IRA had broken its eighteen-month cease-fire he had been asked to conduct a security review of the British Embassy in Dublin. He recalled being met by an officious member of the embassy's security staff, a retired Guards major, who went to great lengths to tell him that the security review was only a matter of form and that the building was quite impregnable.

Twenty-five minutes later, he was standing uninvited in the ambassador's office. The security had been good, but they had neglected the roof. He had simply gained access from a neighbouring building by climbing some scaffolding and the rest was easy. Once inside he had found that, as with most security systems, little thought had been given to preventing an intruder descending from the upper storeys. With luck, McLeod House would be the same.

He was edging his way through the undergrowth when he heard the sound of footsteps heading in his direction. A moving man has difficulty hearing anything but his own footfall, and Fraser took three quick strides back to the fir tree, flattened himself against its rough bark, listening intently for any change in the stride pattern. The steady tread continued.

The reek of tobacco smoke wafted towards him. The

footsteps ceased momentarily. He tensed, holding his breath, aware of the cold sweat on his brow. Then he heard the unseen man hawk and spit, and the bushes rustled and snapped as he continued towards him. When the sentry stepped into view he was so close that Fraser could smell the tobacco on his breath.

Fraser took in the impression of a peaked cap and a slung rifle even as he dropped his hand to clutch his own rifle butt and swing it in a tight arc at the man's nose just below his eyeline. The startled man dropped his cigarette, and instinctively lifted his arm to block the blow. He grunted with pain and shock as the upraised arm took the full force of the steel-plated butt.

For a man taken by surprise he reacted quickly enough. Grasping the AK47 in both hands, he pivoted, thrusting his hips violently against Fraser, who felt himself being propelled through the air by a classic judo hip throw. He landed heavily on his back at the sentry's feet but somehow managed to maintain his grip on the short rifle. He pulled hard on it and, kicking upwards with both feet at the same time, caught the man full in the face.

As he rolled on to his feet he knew that he had to finish this thing fast. His opponent was on his knees, scrabbling for his own rifle. Taking a quick step forward, Fraser lashed out another kick, the force of it almost lifting the man to his feet, before throwing him on to his back. There was no time for mercy. He lifted the AK47 to shoulder level and drove the butt into the prostrate man's face, hitting him where he had originally intended, just below the eyes, driving his nose cartilage into his brain. The man's right leg jerked out violently, then subsided into a series of twitches, as it tried to obey the last instructions from a brain that was already dead.

Fraser pulled his rifle into his shoulder, then slipped off the safety-catch. Swinging his body in a tight arc, he searched for any sound that would indicate danger, but all he could hear was his own thumping heart and air rushing into his gasping lungs. As he got his breathing under control he reviewed his situation.

The dead sentry changed everything, he reasoned. He would be missed, sooner rather than later. When the body was found there would be an immediate alarm and search. He couldn't risk being caught climbing the outer wall when that happened. There was only one other thing to do. He knelt and he began to strip the dead man.

Kirby pulled hard on his cigar, showing no emotion as the medic worked on his arm, but simply asking, 'How bad is it?'

The medic smiled up at him. 'Straight through the meat of your left biceps, Mr Kirby. It will hurt like hell for a few weeks, but there will be no permanent damage. You want something for the pain?'

'No, just clean it up and bandage it. I have to stay frosty until this is over.'

'Anything you say, Mr Kirby. But I'll have to give you a shot to prevent infection.'

Kirby nodded and looked over the medic's shoulder towards Charlotte. 'First hole anybody has ever put into me,' he said, then grimaced as the man pulled the dressing tighter. 'Of all the goddamn places on earth I thought I might catch a piece of lead, the north of Scotland was the last I would have bet money on.'

Charlotte stared back with more defiance than she felt. To her right a squat, heavily built man in combat clothing trained a Beretta automatic on her stomach. She glanced at him quickly, then wished she hadn't. He returned her glance without emotion. His eyes were black, cold pools and she knew then how a drowning man feels looking into the eyes of a shark.

The medic mixed a phial of penicillin and injected the security chief. Kirby pulled his jacket on with difficulty then jerked his head towards the door. The squat man rose and yanked Charlotte roughly to her feet. As she tried to pull her arm free, his hands, like steel claws, only tightened their grip. She yelped with pain.

'Keep your hands off me, you bastard,' she screamed.

She never saw the back-handed slap that knocked her to the floor. Landing heavily, tears in her eyes, she tasted blood in her mouth. The man reached down with nicotine-stained fingers to grasp her hair. In panic she scrambled to her feet, one side of her face a mass of searing pain, only to see him draw back his hand to deliver another blow.

'Stop.'

The man froze, his arm raised to strike, and glanced at Kirby. The security chief shook his head. Charlotte saw the disappointment on her attacker's face as he released her. Turning her around roughly, he pushed her out of the room.

She suppressed a sob as she staggered along the corridor, wiping the blood from her mouth and the tears from her eyes. As she forced herself to ignore the pain in her swelling face and concentrated on her surroundings, she realized for the first time just how quiet the house was. The security chief had phoned Braxton when he had arrived, but, apart from his ugly friend and the medic, she had seen no one since she had been frog-marched through the entrance hall.

Ahead of them Kirby opened the door to the communications room. The squat man handed his gun to him, sat down in front of a powerful radio and pulled on a set of headphones. He spoke into the microphone with an American accent heavily laced with French, asking various call-signs to report. He swore and removed the headphones.

'They've lost him again. He jumped the search line, killed one man. Weaver has no idea where he is now.'

Kirby's face, already pale with pain, stiffened slightly. 'I know where he's heading.' He never took his eyes off Charlotte. 'Get Jackson to man the monitors at the front door. I want everyone else, including the pothole guards, you and the medic, to form up in the dining hall. Sooner or later our friend will turn up. I'll meet you there in ten minutes.'

He pulled his Glock automatic from its shoulder holster and handed the radio operator back his Beretta. The man shoved it into his tight waistband and replaced his earphones. Kirby motioned for Charlotte to leave, prodding her further along the corridor to an expensively furnished room. Kirby nudged her again.

'Sit in the big oak chair.'

Charlotte complied. Behind her she heard a drawer being opened and closed. Then her hands were pulled roughly behind her back and cold metal enclosed her wrists. She jerked her hands and found that heavy handcuffs now secured her to the chair. Kirby stepped round in front of her.

'This is Braxton's private office. He must be seeing off his little civil servant. He wants to talk with you.'

'Go to hell.'

Kirby inclined his head. 'Probably will, Miss Reynolds, but not before you, I think.'

He studied her for several seconds, then stepped closer, placed his good right hand on the arm rest to steady himself and dropped down until his eyes were level with hers. Charlotte squirmed, then relaxed slightly – there seemed to be nothing threatening about his manner.

'Fraser' – he paused, choosing his words carefully – 'I need to know about him.'

'Why, so you can kill him?'

He shook his head and looked down. 'You don't understand. For me it's gone beyond that. I can't believe all this has been an accident. He's a professional, right?'

Charlotte felt compelled to nod.

Kirby slapped his hand on to the arm rest. A smile crossed his face, making him suddenly seem very young.

'I knew it, I knew it – SAS?'

'I don't honestly know.'

He stood up. 'I'd bet money on it.' He walked towards the door, but then stopped and looked back. 'Braxton'll be here in a few minutes. He'll ask you some questions. I advise you to answer. I personally don't enjoy hurting women, but as you already saw, he has some who do.' With that, he left Charlotte to her thoughts.

She rubbed her tongue against the inside of her mouth: the blow she had received had opened a large cut. Taking a deep breath, she threw her weight against the chair. It was futile. The oak frame seemed immovable. She gave up struggling and stared at the ormolu clock dominating the fireplace. In forty minutes Galbraith would be at the front gates. He and Fraser were both still free. She still had a chance. The clock's filigree finger slid forward another minute. Not much of a chance. But a chance all the same.

Galbraith kept watch from the seat of his Land Rover. He had driven to within fifty yards of the main gate with his lights out and now he pondered how long it would be before Johnstone contacted someone at McLeod House about his escape or, worse still, came over himself with half a dozen men. Charlotte and Fraser weren't due at the gate for half an hour but the more he thought about it the more sense it made to act now, before there was any warning to the gatehouse guard. He turned the lights on and drove straight up to the wrought-iron gates. There was no immediate reaction to his arrival. He found his lips suddenly very dry and sweat cooled his face. Had the news of his escape already been passed to the gatehouse? Were the sentries even now watching him over their rifle barrels? He pumped the horn; its sound made his heart lurch. Still no one came. Then he saw movement in the gatehouse and a lone sentry appeared, glanced briefly at the Land Rover, then swung open the gate a little and strolled over to the driver's open window.

'You'll have to wait, buddy. I tried to ring the main house but nobody's answering. Until I get the OK, I can't let anybody . . .'

The sentry bent over, clutching at his eyes. Galbraith leapt from the vehicle, a tear-gas spray in his hand. He grabbed the man by the shoulder to straighten him. Through a searing red mist the sentry had only the vaguest impression of his attacker as Galbraith leaned back and then smashed his forehead into the bridge of his nose.

In seconds, Galbraith had secured his hands behind his back and was dragging him to the guard hut. He took the Colt .45 automatic from the man's shoulder holster, shoved it in his own waistband, then tied the motionless man to a chair with his own belt. Back outside, he threw open both gates, then drove through and parked the Land Rover to one side, where it could not be seen.

There was a second, electronically operated gate fifty yards up from the main entrance. From his previous visits he knew that this was operated from the house. He pulled out the bolt cutters from the back seat The massive jaws sliced through the securing locks with ease. He checked his watch again: just under twenty-five minutes to go. Ahead of him he saw a lone man step from the woods and walk towards the front of the house. He darted back into the shadows. What in God's name were they to do now?

Jackson's foot hurt like hell. He had it propped on a pillow-covered chair as he surveyed the rows of TV monitors. Kirby had called out every able-bodied man for the renewed hunt for Fraser and, like it or not, the walking wounded were being pressed into service. He had been the butt of everyone's jokes since his accident, but now even his rest had been interrupted. He threw a baleful look at his bandaged foot. If he ever got his hands on the limey they were chasing . . .

Movement on one of the monitors caught his eye: Ericsson was coming back from the wood. Jackson looked at his watch in puzzlement. He wasn't due back for at least another half-hour. He swivelled round with difficulty as the huge door to McLeod House opened.

'What are you doing back, Andy? Kirby told you to patrol the woods until Vince relieved you. He'll have your hide for sure if he sees, you ba. . .'

Fraser pointed his automatic at the surprised guard's head. Jackson had a Glock automatic in a shoulder holster under his left arm, and for a moment he thought about reaching for it. But then he looked into Fraser's cold eyes and raised both his hands. He'd already seen what this man had done to his friends. They weren't paying him enough money to commit suicide.

Fraser strode quickly round the table to relieve Jackson of his gun, then, jabbing his own automatic against the man's head, he stepped behind him to survey the empty hall. He noted the lift and the closed dining hall door, from behind which drifted a murmur of voices. Never taking his eyes off the door, he leaned forward to put his mouth close to Jackson's ear.

'If you want to live, answer softly and quickly. Understand?'

Jackson nodded.

'How many men are there in there?'

'Six.'

'Any more expected?'

'Yeah, the pothole guards are coming back.'

'When?'

'Fifteen minutes or so.'

Fraser's eyes drifted to the lift.

'That the only way up?'

'No, there are stairs, right over there to your left.'

'On which floor are they holding the girl?'

'Top.'

'Any more sentries up there?'

Jackson hesitated. Fraser dug his pistol deeper into the side of his neck.

'If there's shooting you'll be the first to die.'

Jackson considered his options and found them limited.

'Just one guard. He sits opposite the lift entrance and . . .'

'Armed?'

'Yeah, a handgun.'

Grabbing Jackson by the scruff of his neck, Fraser hauled him to his feet.

'Let's go.'

Charlotte's wrists were badly chafed from her attempts to slip one of her hands out of the handcuffs. Eventually she had given up. Tears of frustration and pain pricked her eyes. The wall clock showed there was fifteen minutes until she was due to meet Galbraith. Waves of hopelessness swept over her. Then the door opened. She had never met the man who entered before but recognized him immediately from her briefing photographs.

Braxton pulled the heavy, leather armchair from behind his desk so that he could sit facing her. He watched her silently, his eyes penetrating her, forcing her to look away.

'Well, Miss Reynolds, you and your friend Fraser have certainly caused me a few problems.'

She gave him a venomous glance, but refused to answer.

'I want you to understand clearly I need some answers from you. I will get them one way or the other.'

Charlotte drew her head up and remained silent.

Braxton sighed. 'I see you met André: short, dark complexion, smokes cheap French cigarettes. He's seated outside this room. André likes to hurt people. More especially, he likes to hurt women. Although the New Orleans Police don't know it, several of their unsolved female homicides are his handiwork.'

'How do you sleep at night?' Charlotte's words were heavy with disgust.

'I sleep very well, thank you, Miss Reynolds. Are you gonna answer my questions or do I call him in?'

Charlotte remembered her basic training in resistance to interrogation. 'What do you want to know?'

'That's better.' Braxton beamed. 'Who's your controller in SIS?'

'Sir John Kinmont.'

Braxton nodded. 'Oh yeah, pity about him. Knocked down and killed in a car crash just the other day.'

The tears stung her eyes. She had known the old man since childhood. 'You bastard.'

Braxton sighed again. 'A fairly accurate description, Miss Reynolds, but not due to any accident of birth. I'm a completely self-made man. Tell me, what you know about Operation Hades?'

Charlotte looked away as tears streamed down her face.

'Miss Reynolds, you are not a professional. I know you did remarkably well to get this far, but now you have to consider your own position. Galbraith has been arrested by his own Superintendent.'

Charlotte could not suppress a look of surprise. Braxton allowed himself a smile and continued. 'Ah yes, there'll be no cavalry coming to the rescue, I'm afraid. Now, I must ask you for the final time: what do you know about Operation Hades?'

She hesitated. 'We know about the accident. Know you smuggled out contaminated waste from the plant with some spent fuel rods and that Carter helped you separate the waste from the consignment in Customs.'

The clock chimed the quarter, the notes hanging in the air. 'That's all?'

'Yes.'

Braxton laughed. 'I believe you, Miss Reynolds.' His laughter became louder, and he slapped his palm against his knee. 'I believe you. You're not a good enough actress to lie.'

His reaction surprised her. 'What's so funny?'

'*You* are, Miss Reynolds. You don't know what all this is about, do you?'

'Illegal nuclear waste?'

Braxton shook his head. 'Do you think I'd do this just because I had a few kilos of nuclear waste? I could have bought the Energy Commission twice over for the money this has cost me. It's no ordinary nuclear waste, Miss Reynolds – it's Plutonium B.'

18

André was bored. He could hear Braxton talking to the girl through the open door. Hearing her answering his boss, he cursed: he had hoped she would be more stubborn. But it would do her no good in the end: Braxton had promised her to him. His lips peeled back as he savoured the thought; he would have to take her into the woods – no one would hear her there. Then he'd tell her what he was going to do. He loved that the most: the anticipation, seeing the fear in their eyes, the rising and falling of their tits as panic overwhelmed them. First he'd . . . The sound of the lift arriving interrupted his reverie.

He straightened in his chair, surreptitiously nipped out his cigarette and stuffed it in his pocket. The lift door remained closed. He rose quickly, drawing the Beretta from his waistband as he stepped towards the lift. Still the door remained closed. While slipping off the safety-catch of the Beretta, he pressed the door release button and the mottled steel door slid slowly open. He let the Beretta dip slightly as he saw Jackson.

'What the fu. . .?'

André had only a hazy impression of another figure in the lift before his entire body was convulsed with a pain so intense that everything froze. He tried to pull the trigger of his

Beretta, but the heavy, fifteen-shot automatic was a double-action weapon requiring a hefty pull to fire the first round in the chamber. Normally his strong fingers hardly felt the strain; now it seemed as if the trigger was set in concrete. He concentrated all his will, determined to kill, even as death rushed to meet him. The round hammer on the rear of the Beretta moved fractionally as the weapon slipped from his nerveless fingers.

He stared into the man's cold, blue eyes set in an iron-hard face. Then he looked at Jackson, registering the gun in his killer's other hand pointing at Jackson's head, and the fear and horror in his face, before his eyes lost their focus. He heard a noise he'd never heard before and was amazed to realize that it was air rushing out of his own mouth and nose. Blackness enfolded him.

Fraser twisted the Bowie knife as André collapsed, allowing it to slide almost noiselessly from the dead man's body. He'd driven the heavy-bladed knife into his liver, aware that the shock would paralyse and kill him almost instantly. He returned the knife to its scabbard, shifted his automatic into his right hand and motioned for Jackson to leave the lift first. Despite his wound, Jackson complied quickly. As they walked to the open door of Braxton's office Fraser heard Charlotte say, 'Plutonium B . . . I've never heard of it.'

'You're not alone,' Braxton assured her. 'It's supposed not to exist. You're right: there was an accident with the new reactor. It was an experimental design. If it had worked it would have cut production costs by half, but instead it went right off the beam. We had real problems shutting it down; there was nearly a meltdown. We only just got it under control in time, and when we did we discovered Plutonium B.'

Looking through the open door, Fraser saw the tycoon

rubbing his eyes with his finger and thumb as he continued in a flat monotone. 'Plutonium B is the most toxic substance ever created by man. It can't be treated, can't be contained and every three months its toxicity doubles.

'It's growing like a living thing' – his hands spread wide and he shook his head helplessly – 'and we don't know how or why.' He looked down, seemingly preoccupied with the subdued hues of the Kashan carpet.

Fraser recognized something in the man's voice he never expected to hear. Fear. Then Charlotte asked, 'Why did you chose to dump it here?'

'I didn't have long to plan. A nuclear inspection team was on its way, and if they'd discovered the Plutonium B I would've been ruined. There was a shipment of spent fuel rods on the way to Dunston for reprocessing and I smuggled the Plutonium B in with them. That's when I thought about this place, a wilderness next to a nuclear power station. I could store the stuff at Dunston while I put up a security fence around the estate and nobody would suspect a thing. The potholes on the estate are nearly a mile deep: tailor-made for my purposes. Once we get the Plutonium B into the underground cavern we conservatively estimate that we will buy ourselves twenty years before the contamination becomes apparent.'

'Apparent? How?'

Braxton shrugged. 'Seepage. It'll contaminate the drinking water first and then the soil itself.'

'Ragnarök.'

'What did you say?'

'It doesn't matter . . . You'll turn this whole area into a wasteland. Do you understand that?'

Fraser could hear the horror in Charlotte's voice.

'Probably, but by that time I'll have sold my nuclear interests.'

'It's men like you that make God want to cry.'

He sighed. 'You may be right, Miss Reynolds. But you see, I'm just a businessman. Anyhow, soon I intend to disappear entirely.'

'Why did you kill Carter?'

'Like you he thought I was disposing of some regular nuclear waste. Then one of the containers started to leak. That's when he found out it was Plutonium B and came charging up here like some avenging angel, demanding that we tell the authorities.'

'And Fraser's wife?'

Braxton tilted his head slightly. 'That was an accident. She saw my bodyguard Atler kill Carter, which brings me neatly to my next question. Where's Fraser now?'

Fraser pushed Jackson into the room. Braxton's head spun round towards him, but he froze on seeing the gun in Fraser's hand.

'Get up,' Fraser ordered softly, covering both Jackson and Braxton as the tycoon staggered to his feet. Braxton's eyes met Fraser's; he didn't like what he saw there.

'Where are the keys to the handcuffs?' Fraser growled.

Braxton seemed transfixed, his eyes moving between the intruder and the open door. He seemed unable to reply.

'They're in the desk drawer, I think,' Charlotte offered.

'Get them,' Fraser said in the same soft tone.

Braxton scuttled across the parquet flooring, leaned across the desk and slid out the drawer. For the briefest moment, he hesitated.

Fraser's eyes narrowed. 'If that's a gun there I'd really like you to pull it out.'

Braxton's hand emerged clutching a set of small keys. He hurried round behind Charlotte.

His eyes still on the two Americans, Fraser went to the drawer and retrieved a silver-plated .38 snub-nosed Colt Cobra revolver. He threw it to Charlotte, who caught it deftly.

'Put those handcuffs on our wounded friend here and gag him,' he told her.

Charlotte complied quickly and moved to stand beside him.

'How did you get here?'

'Through the front door. "Who Dares Wins". Galbraith should be at the front gate by now. We have about five minutes before the rest of the security team arrive. I just have one more thing to take care of.'

Braxton's mouth dropped open. Charlotte saw Fraser's gun arm tense.

'No.'

She threw her arms around him, knocking the gun slightly downwards, and Braxton let out a sigh of relief. Fraser gave her a look of incomprehension.

'Why not? He killed Lindsey, he must pay for that.'

'He will, he will, but not this way. We need him to say what's going on. You must see that. We need him alive.'

Charlotte let go of Fraser and turned to Braxton.

'Where are your records about the Plutonium B and the people involved in getting it into the country?'

Braxton shut his mouth defiantly, his eyes shifting from Charlotte to Fraser. His eyes slid to the door.

'If you shoot it'll be heard downstairs – neither of you will get out of here alive.'

Charlotte's mouth tightened, 'Do you really think Fraser's

bothered about getting out of here alive? The only thing that's stopping him from killing you is the prospect of seeing you spend what's left of your life behind bars. Now where are those records?'

Braxton stared into Fraser's eyes and knew the truth of Charlotte words. 'There are transit documents in the database, but I don't know how to access them.'

'Don't lie,' said Fraser.

Braxton smiled. 'Having a gun pointed at your head concentrates the mind wonderfully, but I'm not lying. I hire people to take care of things like that.'

Charlotte sat down at the computer and began tapping at the keys.

'Can you get into the database?' Fraser asked.

'Maybe, given time.'

'That's something we haven't got a lot of.'

She grunted something Fraser couldn't understand and continued to tap furiously. Minutes later she cursed quietly and looked up. 'It's no good: all the sensitive files are protected. It could take me hours to hack into them. The only thing I've been able to get up are some shipping manifests, but they're not any . . .' Her voice trailed off and she peered even harder at the screen. 'Got it,' she whispered. 'Yes!'

'What?'

'See here: the shipping weight of Braxton's last shipment of fuel rods. It weighed 1202.5kg when it left the States.'

'So?'

'The recorded weight in at UK Customs was 1002.5kg. Precisely 200kg lighter.'

'You won't be able to prove anything with that,' Braxton said confidently.

'Maybe not,' Charlotte said, glaring at him. 'But it's

hard evidence of malpractice and certainly enough to get an investigation started.' She set up the printer and pressed the print key.

As Braxton watched the first page spew out his face grew clouded. 'Listen, I know things were done, but that's all in the past. We all have to think about the future.'

Charlotte could hardly believe her ears; it was as if he was chairing a congenial boardroom meeting.

'I'm in a position to make financial arrangements that will ensure . . .'

'Be quiet,' Fraser said softly.

Braxton ignored him, and took a small step forward.

'. . . both of you will live the rest of your lives like royalty. You can name . . .'

'Shut it.' This time Fraser's harsh tone silenced Braxton. For a second Charlotte believed he would shoot the man. Then Fraser tossed the automatic from his right hand to his left and held up his hand for Braxton to see. It was shaking. 'You're that close, OK?' The warning was superfluous.

The printer spat out the last page and Charlotte gathered them all together. Then she took a disc from the desk, copied the file on to it, wrapped the disc in a few sheets of printer paper and put it in her pocket. Turning to Fraser, she told him, 'There's a fax machine in the communications room at the end of the corridor. We need to go there before we try for the front gate.'

She stepped cautiously through the open door. The corridor was still empty. Followed by Braxton and the ever-watchful Fraser, she walked with quick, purposeful steps to the communications room, which was deserted. She inserted the printout and dialled a phone number from memory.

'Who are you sending it to?' Fraser asked.

'My ministerial contact.' She looked at him and smiled. 'And some other friends of mine.'

'We should have been at the gate fifteen minutes ago.'

'According to Braxton, Galbraith's been arrested by his own boss. We may have to talk our way out, which is another good reason for keeping him alive.'

The fax machine confirmed transmission and Charlotte dialled in another number.

'How long now?' Fraser asked.

'Just a few more minutes.'

'Be as quick as you can. I've got a feeling things are going to warm up very soon.'

For one of the very few times in his life Galbraith was racked with indecision. He had made his way back to his car, but Charlotte was now over twenty minutes late. Should he stay at the main gate or go and look for her? If he went, he stood the risk of running into some of Kirby's thugs, and he would be no match for them in any kind of encounter. If he stayed, sooner or later somebody was bound to come across him.

He decided to move towards the house. Driving up to the main entrance was out of the question, but he could park short of the house and walk the last twenty yards or so in cover and take a look around. At least it beat sitting and waiting for something to happen.

The driveway was deserted. He saw the squat outline of McLeod House before pulling off to one side and picking his way on foot through the thinning saplings until he could clearly see the façade. Then he heard a noise to his left and saw about ten armed men emerge from the trees, heading towards the steps of the house.

*

Charlotte pulled the printout from the fax machine and hastily folded the sheets and shoved them into her pocket with the disc before gingerly opening the door. No one was outside. She looked back over her shoulder, then back to Fraser. 'Lift or stairs?'

'Stairs. I don't want to get trapped in a lift.'

She stepped up beside him. 'How many of them are there downstairs?'

'At least six . . . probably more by now.'

'Doesn't look too good, does it?'

'Whatever happens, they'll know they've been in a fight.'

Fraser pushed Braxton in front of him. He was about to set off when Charlotte's hand on his arm halted him. He turned his head, and she grabbed his face between both her hands and kissed him full on the lips. Pulling herself from him, she looked into his eyes and whispered, 'I thought you might need that – just in case.'

He smiled. 'Thanks, I did.' He pushed Braxton forward.

The three moved down the hall. Braxton was forced almost to jog to keep up with Fraser's stride behind him. Charlotte opened the connecting door to the staircase. The way was clear. She motioned for them to follow and started down. The staircase, its wide treads worn to a deep, honey-coloured patina, spiralled gracefully to the hall. Keeping to the wall, she made her way down flight by flight.

The stillness around her increased her fear. The entrance hall came into view. She scanned it nervously; it was deserted. As she glanced back at Fraser to ask what he wanted to do, she noticed his eyes change and instantly looked ahead again. Two men came through the front door. One she didn't recognize, the other she did: it was Weaver.

Weaver saw them almost immediately and whipped up the

rifle he was carrying as his companion started to draw an automatic from a shoulder holster. Fraser's gun barked and both men keeled over. The hall was suddenly crammed with armed men. Fire poured at them from half a dozen rifles and pistols. Fraser's voice came from behind her, loud but calm despite the torrent of lead that was being directed at them.

'Get back up behind me,' he yelled.

Keeping flat against the wall once again, she began to edge back up the stairs. Riddled with bullets, the wooden banister to her right was disintegrating.

Galbraith heard the firing and for a second his mind went numb. He had to help, but what could he do? A call to the station was useless and alone he could achieve nothing. He needed squad cars and armed men. He raced back to the Land Rover. He leaned against the vehicle, wheezing almost uncontrollably. All that he had to hand was a megaphone, the bolt cutters and Johnstone's mobile phone. He reached for the phone and threw his eyes up to heaven. 'God, please take pity on fools and desperate policemen.' He poked furiously at the handset.

Charlotte scrambled over Fraser's legs, hardly able to believe she hadn't been hit. As soon as she was past him Fraser grabbed Braxton and stood upright with his gun at his head. The firing stopped.

'The next shot that is fired will be your boss's death warrant. Is Kirby there?' he shouted.

There was a moment's silence. Then a voice answered from below.

'No.'

'Get him, we have some talking to do.' Fraser pulled

Braxton back behind the bend of the stairwell. He looked at Charlotte. 'That's bought us some time at least.'

'What happens when Kirby arrives?' She was surprised how strong her voice was.

Fraser shrugged. 'Let's hope they value their boss's life enough for us to get out of here.'

Twenty minutes crawled by. There were sounds of occasional movement from below them, but no more shots. A man strolled through the open main door as if returning from an evening's walk in the grounds. He was smoking a cigar. He paused to glance at the two dead men just inside the door, then walked to the foot of the staircase.

'I'm Kirby,' he stated flatly.

Fraser edged Braxton out from cover and looked down at the security chief. They exchanged glances. Fraser smiled at his opponent.

'I know who you are,' he told him. 'I saw you in the potholes.'

'You have the advantage over me then. Is he OK?' he said, nodding towards Braxton.

'For the moment.'

Kirby studied him. 'Mind telling me what outfit you're with?'

'22 SAS.'

Kirby nodded, and took a deep pull on his cigar. 'Thought so. You were too damn good to be an amateur. What do you want?'

'I would have thought that was obvious. I want your men to withdraw and give us a clear run to the front gate.'

Kirby shook his head. 'I can't do that.'

'Matt, do . . .'

'Shut up, you fool.' Kirby's voice cut off Braxton's plea.

The tycoon's face took on a look of incredulity. 'Matt, I employ you. You can't . . .'

'You're in no position to order anyone,' Kirby said coldly. His eyes shifted to Fraser. 'It's payback time.'

Behind him men, all armed with rifles, began to file into the hall.

'You've nowhere to run to this time, Fraser,' Kirby said, reaching for his automatic. Fraser tensed, ready to fire and take his chances on a retreat up the stairs. Then they heard a faint, but distinctive sound, travelling a great distance through the clear highland air. Sirens. Kirby's men exchanged glances, then a voice blared over a megaphone.

'This is the police. You are surrounded. Put down your arms and come out with your hands up.'

Kirby reacted instantly. 'The helicopter. Move fast. They can't have enough men to surround the place yet.'

His men scattered, but Kirby stayed. The distinctive thrump, thrump of the rotors half drowned his words. 'Not only are you good, you're lucky. That's what Napoleon always said about his marshals, wasn't it? "Yes, yes, I know he's brilliant, but is he lucky?"' He laughed without warmth and started to make for the door, then looked up again. Fraser read the hatred in his eyes.

'There is just one more thing I . . .' Kirby said, drawing and firing in one movement.

Fraser pushed himself away from Braxton, trying to get his own gun into line, but Kirby was ahead of him, firing two quick shots. Both hit Braxton. The dead man's heavy body slumped into Fraser, making him miss with a quick snap shot. Fraser tried to steady himself for another shot as Kirby fired again.

'No,' Charlotte screamed.

Fraser shoved Braxton's body aside and got a clear target picture. He fired five shots in quick succession. Instinctively he knew he had hit with at least one of them. Kirby staggered, spun round and ran for the door. Fraser's shots tracked him as he jinked across the hall, whining into the air as they ricocheted off the walls. But Kirby was through the door.

Kneeling beside Charlotte, Fraser stared into her eyes. Her pupils were dilated and luminous, almost obscuring her deep green eyes, and her skin felt cold and damp. He searched for the entry wound. Relief surged through him: it was the left side of her chest and she probably had a punctured lung, but that wouldn't be fatal.

She reached up to caress his face. 'I would have liked to have known you a little better.'

'Don't talk. It will be all right, love.'

Fraser knew she could breathe easily enough with one lung, though he would need a waterproof covering to put over the wound to prevent air rushing in, which would cause an embolism and collapse her uninjured lung as well. Perhaps there would be Clingfilm in the kitchen at the bottom of the stairs.

He took Charlotte's hand from his face and carried her down to the bottom of the stairs, where he laid her softly on her injured side before racing to the kitchen. He was back at her side in seconds. Her breathing sounded awful. He wrapped the plastic film round the entry and exit wounds, then wrapped her chest in a makeshift bandage of tea towels. Her breathing sounded a little easier as he turned her once again on to her injured side.

A noise from the doorway made him raise his pistol as a man burst into the hallway below.

'They're running for the helicopter. Christ, if they'd come

out shooting I don't know what I'd have done.' The man saw the gun in Fraser's hand and lifted his hands. 'I'm Galbraith.' He looked at the still form in Fraser's arms. 'Charlotte?' The word was barely a whisper.

'She's alive but badly injured. We need an ambulance fast.'

Galbraith was on the mobile phone instantly.

'It's better if she remains here until the ambulance arrives.'

Fraser stood slowly, glancing at Braxton. Two neat holes punctured his forehead and nothing remained of the back of his skull. He walked to the open doorway. Three police cars swung into the driveway and screeched to a halt. Superintendent Johnstone got out of the leading vehicle. He was armed, as were the two nervous uniformed officers with him. He pointed his revolver at Fraser.

'Armed police. Put down your gun.'

Fraser ignored him and headed towards the helicopter pad.

'Halt or I fire.'

'I wouldn't do that if I were you. You might make him angry.'

Johnstone looked from Fraser's retreating back to his Chief Inspector. Galbraith noted his bewilderment and stepped closer to his former superior. 'It's over. Don't make things worse,' he told him.

Johnstone looked around wildly. 'I want to speak to Mr Braxton immediately.'

'That's going to be difficult, unless you're a medium,' Galbraith said with relish. He leaned towards Johnstone and removed his gun from his unprotesting hand.

Then he looked up at the bewildered officers ranged behind the Superintendent. 'Sergeant, convey Mr Johnstone back to the station and stay with him until a senior officer can sort out this mess.'

The noise from the helicopter increased as its rotors whirled to full power.

Fraser turned to Galbraith.

'Aren't your men going to try and stop them taking off?'

'What men? This is all we've got.'

'You were on your own?'

He nodded.

'What about the sirens?'

Before Galbraith could reply, two ancient, gleaming red and brass fire engines rattled to a stop just in front of them. Finlay MacDonald jumped down, a ludicrous, oversized, ornate fire chief's helmet on his head.

'Where's the fire?'

Galbraith walked up to the part-time fire-fighter. 'Sorry, Finlay. False alarm.'

'False alarm. You as a police officer should know how serious a false alarm is.'

'I'll explain it all in a minute, Finlay.'

A violent down-draught buffeted them as the helicopter took off and then banked slowly over McLeod House. As he shielded his eyes against the loose twigs and grass Fraser saw a pale face against the co-pilot's window. Even at this distance he recognized it immediately. The Sikorsky swung west, towards the coast. As he watched it disappear from sight a weariness almost beyond endurance swept through his body. At the same time a single thought burned itself into his brain.

'One day, Kirby,' he said softly, 'one day.'